SADLIER

VOCABULARY WORKSHOP®

ENRICHED EDITION

Level F

Jerome Shostak

Senior Series Consultant

Vicki A. Jacobs, Ed.D.
Associate Director, Teacher Education Program
Lecturer on Education
Harvard Graduate School of Education
Cambridge, Massachusetts

Series Consultants

Louis P. De Angelo, Ed.D.
Associate Superintendent
Diocese of Wilmington
Wilmington, Delaware

John Heath, Ph.D.
Professor of Classics
Santa Clara University
Santa Clara, California

Sarah Ressler Wright, NBCT
English Department Chair
Rutherford B. Hayes High School
Delaware City Schools, Ohio

Carolyn E. Waters, JD, Ed.S.
ELA/Literacy 6–12 Supervisor
Cobb County School District
Marietta, Georgia

D0060454

Reviewers

The publisher wishes to thank for their comments and suggestions the following teachers and administrators, who read portions of the series prior to publication.

Rivkie Eisen
English Teacher
Ateret Torah High School
Brooklyn, New York

Jennifer Etter
English Dept. Chair
Shorecrest High School
Shoreline, Washington

Eileen Ghastin
English Teacher
John F. Kennedy High School
Bronx, New York

Sheri Goldstein
English Dept. Chair
Ida Crown Jewish Academy
Chicago, Illinois

Claudia Lefkowitz
English Teacher
Central Florida Preparatory
Gotha, Florida

Scott Leventhal
English Teacher, Dept. Chair
Council Rock H. S. South
Holland, Pennsylvania

Jeanne Pellegrino
English Teacher, Dept. Chair
Plantation High School
Plantation, Florida

Jennifer Portilla
English Teacher
Pace Brantley School
Longwood, Florida

Kausam R. Salam, Ph.D.
English Teacher-Dual Credit
Cypress Falls High School
Houston, Texas

Linda Schwartz
English Dept. Chair
Seaford School District
Seaford, New York

Patricia Stack
English Teacher
South Park High School
South Park, Pennsylvania

Barbara Swander Miller
Language Arts Dept. Chair
Cowan Jr/Sr High School
Muncie, Indiana

Stephanie K. Turner
English and French Teacher
St. Ursula Academy
Cincinnati, Ohio

Robert Viarengo
English Dept. Chair
Palma School
Salinas, California

Cover: Concept/Art and Design: MK Advertising and William H. Sadlier, Inc.; Cover pencil: Shutterstock/VikaSuh.
Photo Credits: Interior: age Fotostock/Aleruaro 185 *top*. akg-images/IAM: 51 *top*. Alamy/AF archive: 55; Arco Images GmbH: 184; Asia Photopress: 137 *right*; Chris Pearsall: 51 *right*; Classic Image: 69; ClassicStock: 137 *left*; Danita Delimont: 127 *bottom*; DC Premiumstock: 71 *top*; Global Warming Images: 126 *inset*; Mary Evans Picture Library: 65; Michael Schmeling: 185 *center*; Moviestore Collection Ltd: 31, 107; Nikreates: 37; Photos 12: 59; Pictorial Press Ltd: 79; World History Archive: 50. The Art Archive: 146; Chopin Foundation Warsaw/Collection Dagli Orti: 108 *top*; Hans Christian Andersen Birthplace Odense Denmark/Collection Dagli Orti: 109; Marc Charmet: 141. Art Resource, NY: 131; Marie Mauzy: 103; Scala: 70 *bottom*; Werner Forman: 136 *right*. Associated Press/Fabian Bimmer: 60 *bottom left*. Billy Hathorn: 136 *left*. The Bridgeman Art Library/Private Collection/Ken Welsh: 51 *left*. The Bridgeman Art Library International/Bequest of Winslow Warren: 174; Civil War Archive: 12 *right*. Corbis/Ansel Adams Publishing Rights Trust: 164; Bettmann: 13 *top*, 75, 89 *top*, 97, 113, 135, 151, 165, 189, 193; Christophe Gin: 185 *bottom*; Grand Tour: 155; Hulton-Deutsch Collection: 12 *left*; London Stereoscopic Company: 89 *bottom*; Nancy Kaszerman/ZUMA: 27; Underwood & Underwood: 145; William Manning: 41. Courtesy of The Barnum Museum, Bridgeport, Connecticut: 108 *bottom*. CSA Images: 60, 88 *frames*. Digital Stock: 126 *background*, 164 *background*. Digital Vision: 70 *background*. Everett Collection: 21, 179; Mary Evans/BBC/WGBH/Ronald Grant: 183. Getty Images/Gamma-Keystone: 32 *right*; Jupiterimages: 70 *top center*; Michael Utech: 147 *left*; National Geographic: 93; New York Daily News: 33 *bottom*; Phil Walter: 127 *top*. The Granger Collection, New York: 13 *bottom*, 23 *center*, 23 *bottom*, 175. The Image Works/Marjorie Kamys Cotera/Daemmrich Photography: 22. The Kobal Collection/Granada/Arts Council/Film 4/Buitendijk, JAAP: 117; Paramount/Bad Robot: 17; Universal: 147 *right*. LACMA/Bicentennial gift of Mr. and Mrs. J. M. Schaaf, Mr. and Mrs. William D. Witherspoon, Mr. and Mrs. Charles C. Shoemaker, and Jo Ann and Julian Ganz, Jr.: 174 *top*. musicals101.com: 32 *left*. The New York Public Library, Astor, Lenox and Tilden Foundations/Print Collection, Miriam and Ira D. Wallach Division of Art, Prints and Photographs: 173. Todd-Bingham Picture Collection, Manuscripts and Archives, Yale University: 169. Panos Pictures/G.M.B. Akash: 60 *top*, 61 *top*, 61 *bottom*. Photodisc: 32, 108 *frame*, 146 *background*, 174 *frame*, 175 *frame*. PhotoEdit/Jeff Greenberg: 23 *top*. Shutterstock: BuketGvozdey: 108 *background*; Olena Zaskochenko: 12 *frames*. WHS: 174 *background*. Wikipedia: 33 *top*, 88.

Illustration Credits: Tim Haggerty: 46, 84, 122, 160, 198. Sholto Walker: 98-99.

Copyright © 2012 by William H. Sadlier, Inc. All rights reserved.

This publication, or any part thereof, may not be reproduced in any form, or by any means, including electronic, photographic, or mechanical, or by any sound recording system, or by any device for storage or retrieval of information, without the written permission of the publisher.

Address inquiries to Permissions Department,
William H. Sadlier, Inc.,
9 Pine Street, New York, New York 10005-4700.

S® and **VOCABULARY WORKSHOP**®
are registered trademarks of
William H. Sadlier, Inc.

Printed in the United States of America.
ISBN: 978-0-8215-8011-0
3 4 5 6 7 8 9 10 EB 20 19 18 17 16

For additional online resources, go to vocabularyworkshop.com and enter the Student Access Code: VW12SFYRW83K

CONTENTS

ENRICHED EDITION: New Features

For more than five decades, VOCABULARY WORKSHOP has proven to be a highly successful tool for guiding systematic vocabulary growth and developing vocabulary skills. It has also been shown to help students prepare for standardized tests.

New in this edition are the **Reading Passages, Writing, Vocabulary in Context,** and **Word Study** activities. Nonfiction, high-interest passages use 15 or more of the Unit vocabulary words in context. Two writing prompts require a response to the reading and provide practice in writing for standardized tests. New Vocabulary in Context activities present words from the Unit as they are used in classic works of literature. After every three units, Word Study activities, developed in conjunction with Common Core State Standards requirements, provide practice with idioms, adages, and proverbs, as well as denotation and connotation and classical roots.

Look for the new **QR** (Quick Response) codes on the **Reading Passage** and **Vocabulary in Context** pages. The code can be read with a smartphone camera. To read the QR code, download any free QR code application to a smartphone. Snap the code with a smartphone camera to go directly to iWords for the Unit or an interactive quiz. With iWords you can listen to one word at a time or download all of the words in a Unit to listen to them at your convenience.

The new structure of VOCABULARY WORKSHOP is made up of 15 Units. Each Unit consists of the following sections: a **Reading Passage, Definitions, Choosing the Right Word, Synonyms and Antonyms, Completing the Sentence, Writing,** and **Vocabulary in Context**. Together, these exercises provide multiple and varied exposures to the taught words—an approach consistent with and supportive of research-based findings in vocabulary instruction.

Five **Reviews** cover Vocabulary for Comprehension and Two-Word Completions. Vocabulary for Comprehension is modeled on the reading sections of standardized tests, and as in those tests, it presents reading comprehension questions, including specific vocabulary-related ones, that are based on a reading passage.

A **Final Mastery Test** assesses a selection of words from the year with activities on Synonyms, Antonyms, Analogies, Two-Word Completions, Supplying Words in Context, Word Associations, and Choosing the Right Meaning.

In each level of VOCABULARY WORKSHOP, 300 key words are taught. The words have been selected according to the following criteria: currency and general usefulness; frequency of appearance on recognized vocabulary lists; applicability to, and appearance on, standardized tests; and current grade-level research.

ONLINE COMPONENTS
vocabularyworkshop.com

At **vocabularyworkshop.com** you will find iWords, an audio program that provides pronunciations, definitions, and examples of usage for all of the key words presented in this level of VOCABULARY WORKSHOP. You can listen to one word at a time or, if you wish, download to an MP3 player all of the words of any given Unit. You will then be able to listen to the audio program for that Unit at your convenience.

At **vocabularyworkshop.com** you will also find **interactive vocabulary quizzes, flashcards, games and puzzles** that will help reinforce and enrich your understanding of the key words in this level of VOCABULARY WORKSHOP.

iWords🎧 Audio Program available at **vocabularyworkshop.com**.

VOCABULARY STRATEGY: Using Context

The **context** of a word is the printed text of which that word is part. By studying the word's context, we may find **clues** to its meaning. We might find a clue in the immediate or adjoining sentence or phrase in which the word appears; in the topic or subject matter of the passage; or in the physical features—such as photographs, illustrations, charts, graphs, captions and headings—of a page itself.

The **Vocabulary in Context**, **Vocabulary for Comprehension**, and **Choosing the Right Meaning** exercises that appear in the Units, the Reviews, and Final Mastery Test provide practice in using context to decode unfamiliar words.

Three types of context clues appear in the exercises in this book.

A **restatement clue** consists of a *synonym* for or a *definition* of the missing word. For example:

> Faithfully reading a weekly newsmagazine not only broadens my knowledge of current events and world or national affairs but also _____ my vocabulary.

> **a.** curtails   **b.** enhances   **c.** permeates   **d.** mitigates

In this sentence, *broadens* is a synonym of the missing word, *enhances*, and acts as a restatement clue for it.

A **contrast clue** consists of an *antonym* for or a phrase that means the opposite of the missing word. For example:

> While many of the debutantes wore gowns of heavy satin or velvet, Beatrice's gown was made of a (**gossamer, insular**) spun silk.

In this sentence, *heavy* is an antonym of the missing word, *gossamer*. This is confirmed by the presence of the word *While*, which indicates that the answer must be the opposite of *heavy*.

An **inference clue** implies but does not directly state the meaning of the missing word or words. For example:

> Because Bertie had never taken a flying lesson before, he was placed in the class for _____, but he was a quick learner and _____, and he soon graduated to the next level.

> **a.** adulation . . . irresolute   **c.** penury . . . torpid
> **b.** novices . . . astute   **d.** avarice . . . evanescent

There are a few inference clues in this sentence. The phrase *never taken a flying lesson* indicates that Bertie was a beginner, or *novice*. The phrase *quick learner* suggests that Bertie was *astute*. These words are inference clues because they suggest or imply, but do not directly state, the missing words.

VOCABULARY STRATEGY: Word Structure

Prefixes, **suffixes**, and **roots**, or **bases**, are word parts. One strategy for determining an unknown word's meaning is to "take apart" the word and think about the parts. Study the prefixes and suffixes below to help you find out the meanings of words in which they appear

Prefix	Meaning	Sample Words
com-, con-	together, with	compatriot, contact
de-, dis-	lower, opposite	devalue, disloyal
il-, im-, in-, ir, non-, un-	not	illegal, impossible, inactive, irregular, nonsense, unable
super-	above, greater than	superimpose, superstar

Noun Suffix	Meaning	Sample Nouns
-acy, -ance, -ence, -hood, -ity, -ment, -ness, -ship	state, quality, or condition of, act or process of	adequacy, attendance, persistence, neighborhood, activity, judgment, brightness, friendship
-ant, -eer, -ent, -er, -ian, -ier, -ist, -or	one who does or makes something	contestant, auctioneer, resident, banker, comedian, financier, dentist, doctor
-ation, -ition, -ion	act or result of	organization, imposition, election

Verb Suffix	Meaning	Sample Verbs
-ate	to become, produce, or treat	validate, salivate, chlorinate
-fy, -ify, -ize	to cause, make	liquefy, glorify, legalize

Adjective Suffix	Meaning	Sample Adjectives
-al, -ic,	relating to, characteristic of	natural, romantic
-ful, -ive, -ous	full of, given to, marked by	beautiful, protective, poisonous

A **base** or **root** is the main part of a word to which prefixes and suffixes may be added. On the Classical Roots page of the Word Study section, you will learn more about Latin and Greek roots and the English words that derive from them. The following lists may help you figure out the meaning of new or unfamiliar words.

Greek Root	Meaning	Sample Words
-cryph-, -crypt-	hidden, secret	apocryphal, cryptographer
-dem-, -demo-	people	epidemic, democracy
-gen-	race, kind, origin, birth	generation
-gnos-	know	diagnostic
-lys-	break down	analysis

Latin Root	Meaning	Sample Words
-cap-, -capt-, -cept-, -cip-	take	capitulate, captive, concept, recipient
-cede-, -ceed-, -ceas-, -cess-	happen, yield, go	precede, proceed, decease, cessation
-fac-, -fact-, -fect-, -fic-, -fy-	make	faculty, artifact, defect, beneficial, clarify
-tac-, -tag-, -tang-, -teg-	touch	contact, contagious, tangible, integral
-tain-, -ten-, -tin-	hold, keep	contain, tenure, retinue

For more prefixes, suffixes, and roots, visit **vocabularyworkshop.com**.

VOCABULARY AND READING

Word knowledge is essential to reading comprehension. Your knowledge of word meanings and ability to think carefully about what you read will help you succeed in school and on standardized tests, including the SAT, the ACT, and the PSAT.

New **Reading Passages** provide extra practice with vocabulary words. Vocabulary words are boldfaced to draw students' attention to their uses and contexts. Context clues embedded in the passages encourage students to figure out the meanings of words before they read the definitions provided on the pages directly following the passages.

Students read excerpts from classic literature in the **Vocabulary in Context** exercises. Each excerpt includes one of the Unit vocabulary words as it is used in the original work. Students can use what they learn about the word from its use in context to answer questions on the definition.

The **Vocabulary for Comprehension** exercises in each review consist of a nonfiction reading passage followed by comprehension questions. The passages and questions are similar to those that you are likely to find on standardized tests.

Kinds of Questions

Main Idea Questions generally ask what the passage as a whole is about. Often, but not always, the main idea is stated in the first paragraph of the passage. You may also be asked the main idea of a specific paragraph. Questions about the main idea may begin like this:

- The primary or main purpose of the passage is. . .
- The passage is best described as. . .
- The title that best describes the content of the passage is. . .

Detail Questions focus on important information that is explicitly stated in the passage. Often, however, the correct answer choices do not use the exact language of the passage. They are instead restatements, or paraphrases, of the text.

Vocabulary-in-Context Questions check your ability to use context to identify a word's meaning. Use line references to see how and in what context the word is used. For example:

- **Jejune** (line 3) is best defined as. . .
- The meaning of **winsome** (line 15) is. . .

Use context to check your answer choices, particularly when the vocabulary word has more than one meaning. Among the choices may be two (or more) correct meanings of the word in question. Choose the meaning that best fits the context.

Inference Questions ask you to make inferences or draw conclusions from the passage. These questions often begin like this:

- It can be inferred from the passage that. . .
- The author implies that. . .
- Evidently the author feels that. . .

The inferences you make and the conclusions you draw must be based on the information in the passage. Your own knowledge and reasoning come into play in understanding what is implied and in reaching conclusions that are logical.

Questions About Tone show your understanding of the author's attitude toward the subject of the passage. Words that describe tone, or attitude, are "feeling" words, such as *indifferent, ambivalent, scornful, astonished, respectful*. These are typical questions:

- The author's attitude toward . . . is best described as. . .
- Which word best describes the author's tone?

To determine the tone, pay attention to the author's word choice. The author's attitude may be positive (respectful), negative (scornful), or neutral (ambivalent).

Questions About Author's Technique focus on the way a text is organized and the language the author uses. These questions ask you to think about structure and function. For example:

- The final paragraph serves to. . .
- The author cites . . . in order to . . . .

To answer the questions, you must demonstrate an understanding of the way the author presents information and develops ideas.

Strategies

Here are some general strategies to help you as you read each passage and answer the questions.

- Read the introduction first. The introduction will provide a focus for the selection.

- Be an active reader. As you read, ask yourself questions about the passage—for example: What is this paragraph about? What does the writer mean here? Why does the writer include this information?

- Refer to the passage when you answer the questions. In general, the order of the questions mirrors the organization of the passage, and many of the questions include paragraph or line references. It is often helpful to go back and reread before choosing an answer.

- Read carefully, and be sure to base your answer choices on the passage. There are answer choices that make sense but are not based on the information in the passage. These are true statements, but they are incorrect answers. The correct answers are either restatements of ideas in the text or inferences that can be drawn from the text.

- Consider each exercise a learning experience. Keep in mind that your ability to answer the questions correctly shows as much about your understanding of the questions as about your understanding of the passage.

A verbal analogy expresses a relationship or comparison between sets of words. Normally, an analogy contains two pairs of words linked by a word or symbol that stands for an equal (=) sign. A complete analogy compares the two pairs of words and makes a statement about them. It asserts that the relationship between the first—or key—pair of words is the same as the relationship between the second pair.

In the **Analogies** exercises in the Final Mastery Test, you will be asked to complete analogies that is, to choose the pair of words that best matches or parallels the relationship of the key, or given, pair of words. Here are two examples:

1. maple is to **tree** as
   a. acorn is to oak
   b. hen is to rooster
   c. rose is to flower
   d. shrub is to lilac

2. joyful is to **gloomy** as
   a. cheerful is to happy
   b. strong is to weak
   c. quick is to famous
   d. hungry is to starving

In order to find the correct answer to exercise 1, you must first determine the relationship between the two key words, **maple** and **tree**. In this case, that relationship might be expressed as "a maple is a kind (or type) of tree." The next step is to select from choices a, b, c, and d the pair of words that best reflects the same relationship. The correct answer is (c); it is the only pair whose relationship parallels the one in the key words: A rose is a kind (or type) of flower, just as a maple is a kind (or type) of tree. The other choices do not express the same relationship.

In exercise 2, the relationship between the key words can be expressed as "joyful means the opposite of gloomy." Which of the choices best represents the same relationship? The answer is (b): "strong means the opposite of weak."

Here are examples of some other common analogy relationships:

Analogy	Key Relationship
big is to **large** as **little** is to **small**	**Big** means the same thing as **large**, just as **little** means the same thing as **small**.
brave is to **favorable** as **cowardly** is to **unfavorable**	The tone of **brave** is **favorable**, just as the tone of **cowardly** is **unfavorable**.
busybody is to **nosy** as **klutz** is to **clumsy**	A **busybody** is by definition someone who is **nosy**, just as a **klutz** is by definition someone who is **clumsy**.
cowardly is to **courage** as **awkward** is to **grace**	Someone who is **cowardly** lacks **courage**, just as someone who is **awkward** lacks **grace**.
visible is to **see** as **audible** is to **hear**	If something is **visible**, you can by definition **see** it, just as if something is **audible**, you can by definition **hear** it.
liar is to **truthful** as **bigot** is to **fair-minded**	A **liar** is by definition not likely to be **truthful**, just as a **bigot** is by definition not likely to be **fair-minded**.
eyes are to **see** as **ears** are to **hear**	You use your **eyes** to **see** with, just as you use your **ears** to **hear** with.

There are many different kinds of relationships represented in the analogy questions you will find in the Final Mastery Test, but the key to solving any analogy is to find and express the relationship between the two key words.

*Read the following selection, taking note of the **boldface** words and their contexts. These words are among those you will be studying in Unit 1. As you complete the exercises in this unit, it may help to refer to the way the words are used below.*

The Camera in Wartime
<Textbook Entry>

When crowds gathered at photographer Mathew Brady's New York City studio in late 1862 to gaze at the first images of the Civil War (1861–1865), they became the first witnesses to distant battles. The exhibition did nothing to **assuage** the public's fears about the conflict. Instead, the gruesome, even **lurid**, views of battlefield corpses **elicited** terror and sadness. Photography had brought home the terrible reality of war.

Early Photography

Invented in 1839, the camera played only a minor role in the Mexican-American War (1846–1848) and the Crimean War (1853–1856). Early photographs, called daguerreotypes, were difficult to make; a single exposure took up to 30 minutes and yielded only one low-quality image.

During the **hiatus** between those wars and the American Civil War, photography **transcended** its early limitations. With the new wet plate process, exposures could be made in just a few seconds, and a photographer could mass-produce prints from a single negative. That advance made photography practical—and profitable—and when the Civil War began, a **coalition** of photographers fanned out to cover the action.

Civil War Photography

Most Civil War photographers produced images of individual soldiers. Almost every soldier wanted photos of himself in uniform to send to family and friends. Today, their faces stare out at the viewer from across the centuries: the wide-eyed teen, not yet tested under fire; the **jaded** sergeant, worn-out from the horrors he has witnessed; the **unctuous** junior officer, trying hard to appear sincere.

Civil War portrait of a soldier from the 8th New York Heavy Artillery

Mathew Brady's photographic buggy, circa 1863

Photography quickly gained the **approbation** of military leaders. Art imitates life, after all, so when officials needed photos of bridges, terrain, and armaments to plan their attacks, a skillful photographer became a valuable asset. Photos of surgical procedures were distributed as well, showing doctors new techniques that saved lives in **provincial** field hospitals.

Few Civil War photographs show a battle in progress; action shots were not yet generally possible. Once the fighting was over, however, it was the photographer's **prerogative** to rush in and record the aftermath. Such graphic results tended to highlight the grim toll of the war, and many people eventually took **umbrage** at this emphasis. The courage of the soldiers was moving, but the unrelenting carnage was difficult to view.

Marines land on the coast of Normandy the day after D-Day: June 7, 1944.

Mathew Brady and Alexander Gardner

A few Civil War photographers should be singled out for their **meritorious** efforts. Mathew Brady (1823–1896) took thousands of photographs of wartime leaders and battle scenes, and his images continue to help historians better understand the Civil War era. Inspired to document the entire war, Brady conducted his photographic work at his own expense. When federal officials refused to buy his prints, Brady **expostulated** with them to no avail, and he died penniless.

Alexander Gardner (1821–1882) was Brady's assistant in Washington, D.C. When the Civil War began, Gardner successfully **interceded** with President Lincoln, getting him to allow photographers to accompany the army. Gardner himself traveled with Union forces to photograph the battles at Antietam, Gettysburg, and Petersburg. Never **hackneyed** or dull, Gardner's images offered fresh insights into the reality of modern warfare.

Photography in Later Years

In contrast to Civil War photography, the photographic records of the Spanish-American War (1898) and World War I (1914–1918) are relatively limited. Beginning with World War II (1939–1945), however, combat photographers consistently traveled with the troops, risking their lives to capture wartime events. In addition to clarifying the details of every battle, war photographs have depicted the harsh realities endured by ordinary soldiers and helped build support for the war effort on the home front.

W. Eugene Smith (1918–1978), American WWII photographer, on the island of Okinawa, 1945

Snap the code, or go to **vocabularyworkshop.com**

Definitions

Note the spelling, pronunciation, part(s) of speech, and definition(s) of each of the following words. Then write the word in the blank spaces in the illustrative sentence(s) following. Finally, study the lists of synonyms and antonyms.

1. approbation
(ap rə bā' shən)

(*n.*) the expression of approval or favorable opinion, praise; official approval

My broad hint that I had paid for the lessons myself brought smiles of _____ from all the judges at the piano recital.

SYNONYMS: sanction
ANTONYMS: disapproval, condemnation, censure

2. assuage
(ə swāj')

(*v.*) to make easier or milder, relieve; to quiet, calm; to put an end to, appease, satisfy, quench

Her eyes told me that more than a few well-chosen words would be needed to _____ her hurt feelings.

SYNONYMS: mitigate, slake, allay
ANTONYMS: intensify, aggravate, exacerbate

3. coalition
(kō ə lish' ən)

(*n.*) a combination, union, or merger for some specific purpose

The various community organizations formed a _____ to lobby against parking laws.

SYNONYMS: alliance, league, federation, combine
ANTONYM: splinter group

4. decadence
(de' kə dəns)

(*n.*) decline, decay, or deterioration; a condition or period of decline or decay; excessive self-indulgence

Some viewed her love of chocolate as _____ because she ate two candy bars a day.

SYNONYMS: degeneration, corruption
ANTONYMS: rise, growth, maturation

5. elicit
(ē lis' it)

(*v.*) to draw forth, bring out from some source (such as another person)

My attempt to _____ information over the phone was met with a barrage of irrelevant recordings.

SYNONYMS: evoke, extract, educe
ANTONYMS: repress, quash, squelch, stifle

6. expostulate
(ik späs' chə lāt)

(*v.*) to attempt to dissuade someone from some course or decision by earnest reasoning

Shakespeare's Hamlet finds it useless to _____ with his mother for siding with his stepfather.

SYNONYMS: protest, remonstrate, complain

7. hackneyed
(hak′ nēd)

(*adj.*) used so often as to lack freshness or originality

The Great Gatsby tells a universal story without being marred by _____ prose.

SYNONYMS: banal, trite, commonplace, corny
ANTONYMS: new, fresh, novel, original

8. hiatus
(hī ā′ təs)

(*n.*) a gap, opening, break (in the sense of having an element missing)

I was awakened not by a sudden sound but by a _____ in the din of traffic.

SYNONYMS: pause, lacuna; ANTONYMS: continuity, continuation

9. innuendo
(in yü en′ dō)

(*n.*) a hint, indirect suggestion, or reference (often in a derogatory sense)

Those lacking the facts or afraid of reprisals often tarnish an enemy's reputation by use of _____.

SYNONYMS: insinuation, intimation; ANTONYM: direct statement

10. intercede
(in tər sēd′)

(*v.*) to plead on behalf of someone else; to serve as a third party or go-between in a disagreement

She will _____ in the dispute between the two children, and soon they will be playing happily again.

SYNONYMS: intervene, mediate

11. jaded
(jā′ did)

(*adj.*) wearied, worn-out, dulled (in the sense of being satiated by excessive indulgence)

The wilted handclasp and the fast-melting smile mark the _____ refugee from too many parties.

SYNONYMS: sated, surfeited, cloyed
ANTONYMS: unspoiled, uncloyed

12. lurid
(lür′ əd)

(*adj.*) causing shock, horror, or revulsion; sensational; pale or sallow in color; terrible or passionate in intensity or lack of restraint

Bright, sensational, and often _____, some old-time movie posters make today's newspaper ads look tame.

SYNONYMS: gruesome, gory, grisly, baleful, ghastly
ANTONYMS: pleasant, attractive, appealing, wholesome

13. meritorious
(mer i tôr′ ē əs)

(*adj.*) worthy, deserving recognition and praise

Many years of _____ service could not dissuade him from feeling that he had not chosen work that he liked.

SYNONYMS: praiseworthy, laudable, commendable
ANTONYMS: blameworthy, reprehensible

14. petulant
(pech' ə lənt)

(*adj.*) peevish, annoyed by trifles, easily irritated and upset

An overworked parent may be unlikely to indulge the complaints of a _____ child.

SYNONYMS: irritable, testy, waspish; ANTONYMS: amiable, placid

15. prerogative
(prē räg' ə tiv)

(*n.*) a special right or privilege; a special quality showing excellence

She seemed to feel that a snooze at her desk was not an annoying habit but the _____ of a veteran employee.

SYNONYMS: perquisite, perk

16. provincial
(prə vin' shəl)

(*adj.*) pertaining to an outlying area; local; narrow in mind or outlook, countrified in the sense of being limited and backward; of a simple, plain design that originated in the countryside; (*n.*) a person with a narrow point of view; a person from an outlying area; a soldier from a province or colony

The banjo, once thought to be a _____ product of the Southern hills, actually came here from Africa.

At first, a _____ may do well in the city using charm alone, but charm, like novelty, wears thin.

SYNONYMS: (*adj.*) narrow-minded, parochial, insular, naive
ANTONYMS: (*adj.*) cosmopolitan, broad-minded

17. simulate
(sim' yə lāt)

(*v.*) to make a pretense of, imitate; to show the outer signs of

Some skilled actors can _____ emotions they might never have felt in life.

SYNONYMS: pretend, affect

18. transcend
(tran send')

(*v.*) to rise above or beyond, exceed

A great work of art may be said to _____ time, and it is remembered for decades, or even centuries.

SYNONYMS: surpass, outstrip

19. umbrage
(em' brəj)

(*n.*) shade cast by trees; foliage giving shade; an overshadowing influence or power; offense, resentment; a vague suspicion

She hesitated to offer her opinion, fearing that they would take _____ at her criticism.

SYNONYMS: irritation, pique; ANTONYMS: pleasure, delight, satisfaction

20. unctuous
(əŋk' chü əs)

(*adj.*) excessively smooth or smug; trying too hard to give an impression of earnestness, sincerity, or piety; fatty, oily; pliable

Her constant inquiring about the health of my family at first seemed friendly, later merely _____.

SYNONYMS: mealymouthed, fawning, greasy; ANTONYMS: gruff, blunt

Choosing the Right Word

*Select the **boldface** word that better completes each sentence. You might refer to the selection on pages 12–13 to see how most of these words are used in context.*

1. I enjoy science-fiction movies, as they provide a short but exciting (**umbrage, hiatus**) from the problems of everyday life.

2. The magnificence of the scene far (**simulated, transcended**) my ability to describe it in words.

3. My teacher can (**simulate, elicit**) some degree of interest and attention from even the most withdrawn children.

4. The defense attorney quickly realized that the witness's statement was filled with (**innuendo, coalition**), not facts.

Chris Pine as James T. Kirk and Zachary Quinto as Mr. Spock in the 2009 movie update of the 1960s televison series *Star Trek*.

5. His skillful use of academic jargon and fashionable catchphrases could not conceal the essentially (**hackneyed, meritorious**) quality of his ideas.

6. At the Senior Prom, my sister and most of her friends were glad that men are no longer expected to take the (**prerogative, hiatus**) in choosing dance partners.

7. Perhaps it will (**expostulate, assuage**) your fright if I remind you that everyone must try something for the first time at some point in his or her life.

8. How can you accuse me of employing (**umbrage, innuendo**) when I am saying in the plainest possible language that I think you're a crook?

9. The newspaper account of the tragedy was quite sensational and filled with (**lurid, provincial**) details about the accident.

10. Who would have thought he would take (**prerogative, umbrage**) at an e-mail from a friend who wanted only to help?

11. After watching four TV football games on New Year's Day, I was (**jaded, hackneyed**) with the pigskin sport for weeks to come.

12. We cannot know today what sort of accent Abraham Lincoln had, but it may well be that there was a decidedly (**meritorious, provincial**) twang to his speech.

13. Popularity polls seem to be based on the mistaken idea that the basic task of a political leader is to win immediate (**approbation, coalition**) from the people.

14. The most (**meritorious, lurid**) form of charity, according to the ancient Hebrew sages, is to help a poor person to become self-supporting.

15. They try to "prove" the (**umbrage, decadence**) of modern youth by emphasizing everything that is bad and ignoring whatever is good.

16. I truly dislike the kind of sensational popular biography that focuses solely on the more (**lurid, hackneyed**) or scandalous aspects of a superstar's career.

17. On the air the star seemed calm, but he privately sent (**petulant, jaded**) notes to those who gave him bad reviews.

18. When the (**umbrage, hiatus**) in the conversation became embarrassingly long, I decided that the time had come to serve the sandwiches.

19. I prefer reading about modest and sympathetic characters rather than those who are contemptuous and (**lurid, jaded**).

20. The American two-party system almost always makes it unnecessary to form a (**hiatus, coalition**) of minority parties to carry on the government.

21. I see no point in (**expostulating, simulating**) with a person who habitually refuses to listen to reason.

22. Apparently mistaking us for the millionaire's children, the hotel manager overwhelmed us with his (**petulant, unctuous**) attentions.

23. Because she had just received a large bonus, Joan felt it was her (**decadence, prerogative**) to purchase a luxury convertible car.

24. To impress her newly made friends, she (**simulated, assuaged**) an interest in modern art, of which she knew nothing.

25. If you try to (**elicit, intercede**) in a friends' quarrel, you will only make things worse.

Synonyms

*Choose the word from this unit that is the same or most nearly the same in meaning as the **boldface** word or expression in the phrase. Write that word on the line. Use a dictionary if necessary.*

1. a lifestyle of **intemperance**   decadence

2. an **implication** not supported by fact   innuendo

3. **depleted** by too much networking   jaded

4. impolite and **snappish** attitude   petulant

5. a **benefit** of her rank   perogative

6. exploding in **annoyance**   umbrage

7. unceasing and **servile** modesty   _____

8. **feign** a reconciliation   simulate

9. **alleviate** his worst fears   _____

10. seeking the boss's **commendation**   _____

✗

Antonyms

*Choose the word from this unit that is most nearly opposite in meaning to the **boldface** word or expression in the phrase. Write that word on the line. Use a dictionary if necessary.*

1. living a life of sacrifice and **self-denial**   perogative

2. **genuinely express** joy over a coworker's promotion   _____

3. such a **sedate** and self-controlled child   _____

4. a record of **discreditable** actions   _____

5. a lawyer who offers **incontestable proof**   _____

✗
Completing the Sentence

From the words in this unit, choose the one that best completes each of the following sentences. Write the word in the space provided.

1. In an age when the United States has truly global responsibilities, we cannot afford to have leaders with _provincial_ points of view.

2. I take no _____ at your personal remarks, but I feel you would have been better advised not to make them.

3. Forever humbling himself and flattering others, Dickens's Uriah Heep is famously _____.

4. During the brief _____ in the music, someone's ringing cell phone split the air.

5. If you cannot meet the college's entrance requirements, it will be futile to have someone _____ on your behalf.

6. Weakened militarily, and with a large part of the population living on free "bread and circuses," the once mighty Roman Empire now entered a period of _____.

7. The midnight fire in our apartment building cast a(n) _____, unearthly light on the faces of the firefighters struggling to put it out.

8. The manager expressed her unfavorable opinion of the job applicant by _____ rather than by direct statement.

9. The issue of good faith that your conduct raises far _____ the specific question of whether or not you are responsible for the problem.

10. If you take pride in expressing yourself with force and originality, you should not use so many _____ phrases.

11. I certainly appreciate your praise, but I must say that I can see nothing so remarkably _____ in having done what any decent person would do.

12. His confidence grew as he received clear signs of the _____ of his superiors.

13. I feel that, as an old friend, I have the _____ of criticizing your actions without arousing resentment.

14. Various insects have a marvelous capacity to protect themselves by _____ the appearance of twigs and other objects in their environment.

15. Of course you have a right to ask the waiter for a glass of water, but is there any need to use the _____ tone of a spoiled child?

16. The only way to defeat the party in power is for all the reform groups to form a(n) _____ and back a single slate of candidates.

17. Since I don't like people who play favorites in the office, I have frequently _____ against such behavior with my superiors.

18. Although we tried to express our sympathy, we knew that mere words could do nothing to _____ her grief.

19. In the question-and-answer session, we tried to _____ from the candidates some definite indication of how they proposed to reduce the national debt.

20. Their tastes have been so _____ by luxurious living that they seem incapable of enjoying the simple pleasures of life.

Writing: Words in Action

1. Look back at "The Camera in Wartime" (pages 12–13). Imagine that you are Mathew Brady, trying to convince federal officials to purchase prints of the thousands of photographs that you have taken of the Civil War. Write a letter to government officials, persuading them of the historical merit of your work, and explain why your photographs should become part of a national archive. Use at least two details from the passage and three unit words.

2. Civil War photographers were able to record only the disturbing aftermath of war. Today, journalists can provide not only photographs but also live video of battles. What are the drawbacks to or benefits of having the stark reality of war brought into people's homes? Write an essay in which you support your opinion with your own observations, studies, personal experience, and the reading (pages 12–13). Write at least three paragraphs, and use three or more words from this unit.

Vocabulary in Context

Literary Text

The following excerpts are from **David Copperfield** *by Charles Dickens. Some of the words you have studied in this unit appear in* **boldface** *type. Complete each statement below the excerpt by circling the letter of the correct answer.*

1. "You are a very remarkable man, Dick!" said my aunt, with an air of unqualified **approbation**; "and never pretend to be anything else, for I know better!"

    Someone who speaks with **approbation** is
    a. proud
    b. humble
    c. arrogant
    d. judgmental

2. Her quiet interest in everything that interested Dora; her manner of making acquaintance with Jip (who responded instantly); her pleasant way, when Dora was ashamed to come over to her usual seat by me; her modest grace and ease, **eliciting** a crowd of blushing little marks of confidence from Dora; seemed to make our circle quite complete.

    The act of **eliciting** involves
    a. putting off
    b. calling forth
    c. diminishing
    d. prolonging

3. I had had a hard day's work, and was pretty well **jaded** when I came climbing out, at last, upon the level of Blackheath. It cost me some trouble to find out Salem House; but I found it....

    After a hard day's work, a **jaded** person is
    a. invigorated
    b. anxious
    c. disappointed
    d. exhausted

4. Here and there, some early lamps were seen to twinkle in the distant city; and in the eastern quarter of the sky the **lurid** light still hovered. But, from the greater part of the broad valley interposed, a mist was rising like a sea, which, mingling with the darkness, made it seem as if the gathering waters would encompass them.

    A **lurid** light is
    a. bright
    b. scenic
    c. pallid
    d. vivid

Bob Hoskins plays Micawber and Daniel Radcliffe plays young David Copperfield in the 1999 TV miniseries, *David Copperfield*.

5. ...[I] faced about for Greenwich, which I had understood was on the Dover Road: taking very little more out of the world, towards the retreat of my aunt, Miss Betsey, than I had brought into it, on the night when my arrival gave her so much **umbrage**.

    A person filled with **umbrage** is NOT
    a. annoyed
    b. pleased
    c. offended
    d. bitter

Snap the code, or go to **vocabularyworkshop.com**

*Read the following selection, taking note of the **boldface** words and their contexts. These words are among those you will be studying in Unit 2. As you complete the exercises in this unit, it may help to refer to the way the words are used below.*

Why Vote?

<Persuasive Essay>

It is dispiriting to acknowledge the lack of interest that citizens of the United States display when it comes to exercising their right to vote. Many eligible voters, nearly 40 percent, in fact, stayed home in the last presidential election, while at the turn of the twentieth century there was an 80 percent turnout rate for presidential elections. Why has such **lassitude permeated** a society that once was vigorous and energetic about voting?

Nonvoters contend that their vote makes little difference and that they cannot vote because candidates are all loud-mouthed, **bombastic**, and dishonest. Such nonvoters **surmise** that politicians, once elected, act in their own best interests and not in the interests of the people who put them in office. Perhaps they find examples of such behavior among elected officials, but the right to vote is one that should be exercised and appreciated regardless of personal opinion about the characters of the politicians. What nonvoters do not recognize is the plight of people who cannot vote at all. Over many **millennia** and in societies all across the globe, voting was not regarded as an **intrinsic** and inherent right of citizens—except in rare instances. First, absolute monarchs ruled and made decisions by claiming the divine right of kings they believed they alone enjoyed. Aristocrats concurred, and,

like the czars, queens, kings, and emperors they served, they believed that common people were too **callow** and uneducated to govern themselves. Unless these rulers and their scions were compassionate and astute, life for their powerless subjects was a struggle. The same was true for citizens ruled by unrestrained, powerful tyrants, like Nazi Germany's Adolf Hitler and Russia's Joseph Stalin. Even in the emerging democracy in America, the country's founders vigorously debated who could and could not become enfranchised. In 1789, only white men who owned property could rightfully take part in the voting process—hardly the **epitome** of democracy, but a start.

Some nonvoters **inveigh** against the Electoral College, claiming that this body of electors, not the majority of individual voters, actually chooses the President. Under the current system, voters in presidential elections vote not for a candidate but for a slate of electors who are affiliated with a certain party and who promise to cast their ballots for that party's standard-bearer. In a very closely contested election, a candidate with a slight majority of popular votes might lose the election because of the way the Electoral College has voted. This has happened more than once in the country's history.

Today, in many countries, totalitarian dictators still make all decisions for the citizenry **ex officio**, whether or not the people support those decisions. In such societies, citizens are helpless against the **stringent** laws and rigid strictures that **infringe** upon most aspects of their lives. Those residing in one-party "democracies," in which autocrats pay lip service to democratic ideals but treat opposing candidates as **interlopers**, have it no better. Nonvoters should be urgently **exhorted** to consider the alternatives to democracy before they refuse to go to the polls to cast a ballot.

Voting is a process, not a panacea. A single vote will neither herald positive change nor instantly **ameliorate** poor conditions, but voting is the best chance to achieve either outcome. In America, responsible citizens are granted the right to vote at age eighteen; and this right is a privilege and a duty that should be exercised and protected.

Left: A college student encourages people to vote, October 2008. Above: A man registers to vote in Florida.

Snap the code, or go to **vocabularyworkshop.com**

The Presidential campaign of 1928, with Al Smith, Democrat, versus Herbert Hoover, Republican

Definitions

Note the spelling, pronunciation, part(s) of speech, and definition(s) of each of the following words. Then write the word in the blank spaces in the illustrative sentence(s) following. Finally, study the lists of synonyms and antonyms.

1. ameliorate
(ə mēl' yə rāt)

(v.) to improve, make better, correct a flaw or shortcoming

A hot meal can _____ the discomforts of even the coldest day.

SYNONYMS: amend, better; ANTONYMS: worsen, aggravate, exacerbate

2. aplomb
(ə pläm')

(n.) poise, assurance, great self-confidence; perpendicularity

Considering the family's tense mood, you handled the situation with _____.

SYNONYMS: composure, self-possession, levelheadedness
ANTONYMS: confusion, embarrassment, abashment

3. bombastic
(bäm bas' tik)

(adj.) pompous or overblown in language; full of high-sounding words intended to conceal a lack of ideas

He delivered a _____ speech that did not even address our problems.

SYNONYMS: inflated, highfalutin, pretentious
ANTONYMS: unadorned, simple, plain, austere

4. callow
(kal' ō)

(adj.) without experience; immature, not fully developed; lacking sophistication and poise; without feathers

They entered the army as _____ recruits and left as seasoned veterans.

SYNONYMS: green, raw, unfledged, inexperienced
ANTONYMS: mature, grown-up, polished, sophisticated

5. drivel
(driv' əl)

(n.) saliva or mucus flowing from the mouth or nose; foolish, aimless talk or thinking; nonsense; (v.) to let saliva flow from the mouth; to utter nonsense or childish twaddle; to waste or fritter away foolishly

To me, my dream made perfect sense, but when I told it to my friend, it sounded like _____.

Knowing that his time was nearly up, we kept silent and let him _____ on.

SYNONYMS: (n.) balderdash, tommyrot; (v.) slaver

6. epitome
(i pit' ə mē)

(n.) a summary, condensed account; an instance that represents a larger reality

Admitting when you have been fairly defeated is the _____ of sportsmanship.

SYNONYMS: abstract, digest, archetype

7. exhort
(eg zôrt′)

(*v.*) to urge strongly, advise earnestly

With dramatic gestures, our fans vigorously
_____ the team to play harder.

SYNONYMS: entreat, implore, adjure
ANTONYMS: discourage, advise against, deprecate

8. ex officio
(eks ə fish′ ē ō)

(*adj.*, *adv.*) by virtue of holding a certain office

The President is the _____ commander-in-chief
of the armed forces in time of war.

9. infringe
(in frinj′)

(*v.*) to violate, trespass, go beyond recognized bounds

If you continue to _____ on my responsibilities,
will you also take the blame for any mistakes?

SYNONYMS: encroach, impinge, intrude
ANTONYMS: stay in bounds, comply

10. ingratiate
(in grā′ shē āt)

(*v.*) to make oneself agreeable and thus gain favor or acceptance
by others (sometimes used in a critical or derogatory sense)

It is not a good idea to _____ oneself by
paying cloying compliments.

SYNONYMS: cozy up to, curry favor with; ANTONYMS: humiliate oneself

11. interloper
(in′ tər lōp ər)

(*n.*) one who moves in where he or she is not wanted or has no
right to be, an intruder

The crowd was so eager to see the band perform that they
resented the opening singer as an _____.

SYNONYMS: trespasser, meddler, buttinsky

12. intrinsic
(in trin′ sik)

(*adj.*) belonging to someone or something by its very nature,
essential, inherent; originating in a bodily organ or part

It had been my father's favorite book when he was my age, but
for me it held little _____ interest.

SYNONYMS: immanent, organic; ANTONYMS: extrinsic, external, outward

13. inveigh
(in vā′)

(*v.*) to make a violent attack in words, express strong disapproval

You should not _____ against the plan with
quite so much vigor until you have read it.

SYNONYMS: harangue, remonstrate; ANTONYMS: acclaim, glorify, extol

14. lassitude
(las′ ə tüd)

(*n.*) weariness of body or mind, lack of energy

On some days I am overcome by _____ at
the thought of so many more years of schooling.

SYNONYMS: fatigue, lethargy, torpor, languor
ANTONYMS: energy, vitality, animation, liveliness

15. millennium
(*pl.*, **millennia**)
(mə len' ē əm)

(*n.*) a period of one thousand years; a period of great joy
In 1999 an argument raged over whether 2000 or 2001 would mark the beginning of the new _____.
SYNONYMS: chiliad, golden age; ANTONYMS: doomsday

16. occult
(ə kəlt')

(*adj.*) secret, hidden from view; not detectable by ordinary means; mysterious, magical, uncanny; (*v.*) to hide, cover up; eclipse; (*n.*) matters involving the supernatural
Astronomers did not notice the small moon, which was often _____ by the planet around which it orbited.
Much of his talk about the _____ seems grounded in nothing but trick photography and folklore.
SYNONYMS: (*adj.*) esoteric, abstruse, arcane
ANTONYMS: (*adj.*) mundane, common, public, exoteric

17. permeate
(pər' mē āt)

(*v.*) to spread through, penetrate, soak through
The rain _____ all of my clothing and reduced the map in my pocket to a pulpy mass.

18. precipitate
(*v.*, pri sip' ə tāt; *adj.*, *n.*, pri sip' ət ət)

(*v.*) to fall as moisture; to bring about suddenly; to hurl down from a great height; to give distinct form to; (*adj.*) characterized by excessive haste; (*n.*) moisture; the product of an action or process
Scholars often disagree over which event or events _____ an historic moment.
I admit that my outburst was _____.
Too many eggs in this particular pudding will leave a messy _____ in the baking pan.
SYNONYMS: (*v.*) provoke, produce; (*adj.*) reckless, impetuous
ANTONYMS: (*adj.*) wary, circumspect

19. stringent
(strin' jənt)

(*adj.*) strict, severe; rigorously or urgently binding or compelling; sharp or bitter to the taste
Some argue that more _____ laws against speeding will make our streets safer.
SYNONYMS: stern, rigorous, tough, urgent
ANTONYMS: lenient, mild, lax, permissive

20. surmise
(sər mīz')

(*v.*) to think or believe without certain supporting evidence; to conjecture or guess; (*n.*) likely idea that lacks definite proof
I cannot be sure, but I _____ that she would not accept my apology even if I made it on my knees.
The police had no proof, nothing to go on but a suspicion, a mere _____.
SYNONYMS: (*v.*) infer, gather; (*n.*) inference, presumption

Choosing the Right Word

Select the **boldface** word that better completes each sentence. You might refer to the selection on pages 22–23 to see how most of these words are used in context.

1. Marian Wright Edelman has never succumbed to (**drivel, lassitude**) but has instead remained a tireless advocate of children's rights since the 1960s.

2. In stating that "All men are created equal and endowed . . . with certain inalienable rights," the Declaration of Independence proclaims the (**intrinsic, callow**) value of every human being.

3. The large trees that surrounded the strange mansion (**occulted, ameliorated**) our view of the building.

4. We are all ready and willing to do what must be done; what we need is leadership—not (**exhortation, aplomb**)!

5. In this situation we cannot act on the basis of what may be (**surmised, inveighed**), but only in accordance with what is definitely known.

Marian Wright Edelman, a lawyer and champion of children's rights, established the Children's Defense Fund in 1973.

6. One way to (**ingratiate, ameliorate**) your fears of giving a speech is to put your audience at ease with a personal anecdote.

7. A sour odor of decay, stale air, and generations of living (**permeated, precipitated**) every corner of the old tenement.

8. I (**surmised, infringed**) that you did well on your test when you bolted through the front door as though you had just won the lottery.

9. When the bridge suddenly collapsed in the high winds, the people on it at the time were (**inveighed, precipitated**) to their deaths in the watery abyss below.

10. "I'm sure your every wish will be granted," I assured the demanding child, my tongue firmly in my check, "when and if the (**exhortation, millennium**) ever comes!"

11. Although the music—an étude by Schumann—was not familiar to him, the pianist followed the sheet music and played the piece with great (**aplomb, lassitude**).

12. The song had a pleasant, (**stringent, ingratiating**) melody that gained it quick popularity and then caused it to be forgotten just as quickly.

13. I trust that we shall have the will to improve what can now be improved and the patience to bear what cannot now be (**ameliorated, surmised**).

14. After the unexpected defeat, the members of the team wanted to be alone and regarded anyone who entered the locker room as a(n) (**interloper, lassitude**).

15. I can usually forgive a(n) (**callow, ex officio**) display of feeble jokes and showing off—but not by someone who has passed his fortieth birthday!

16. The publisher will take prompt legal action against anyone who (**inveighs, infringes**) on the copyright of this book.

17. This famous definition by a British general (**epitomizes, infringes**) the nature of war: "Long periods of intense boredom punctuated by short periods of intense fear."

18. If you desire a strong garlic flavor that (**precipitates, permeates**) the dish, use fresh, minced garlic rather than garlic powder.

19. After the speaker had droned on pointlessly for half an hour, an angry man in the front row stood up and said, "Must we continue to listen to all this childish (**lassitude, drivel**)?"

20. Kathy baked cookies for her book club, hoping to (**surmise, ingratiate**) herself so that she would be nominated as president.

21. Because I believe in spreading governmental powers among several officials, I am opposed to having the Mayor serve as (**intrinsic, ex officio**) head of the Board of Education.

22. His message may seem (**bombastic, callow**), but there is a solid framework of practical ideas underlying the rather pompous language.

23. Do we need new laws to combat crime, or rather, more (**ingratiating, stringent**) enforcement of the laws we already have?

24. It is easy to (**inveigh, precipitate**) against "dirty politics," but less easy to play a positive role, however small, in the political process.

25. She handled a potentially embarrassing situation with cool (**drivel, aplomb**).

 **Synonyms**
*Choose the word from this unit that is the same or most nearly the same in meaning as the **boldface** word or expression in the phrase. Write that word on the line. Use a dictionary if necessary.*

1. hints of a **concealed** presence   _____

2. a stain that **leaked through**   _____

3. overdramatic, **high-flown** language   _____

4. the **model** of what not to wear   _____

5. a smile meant to **flatter**   _____

6. to **rail** against a harmless mistake   _____

7. a line delivered with **ease**   _____

8. thought the idea to be **hogwash**   _____

9. an **imperative** requirement   _____

10. to **create** a reaction   _____

Antonyms

*Choose the word from this unit that is most nearly opposite in meaning to the **boldface** word or expression in the phrase. Write that word on the line. Use a dictionary if necessary.*

1. to **alienate** your friends _____

2. **uncover** the truth _____

3. a **cautious** move on the chess board _____

4. listen to **wisdom** _____

5. a performance filled with **clumsiness** _____

Completing the Sentence

From the words in this unit, choose the one that best completes each of the following sentences. Write the word in the space provided.

1. The prophets of old fervently _____ the people to amend their lives.

2. I refuse to accept the idea that conditions in this slum have deteriorated so far that nothing can be done to _____ them.

3. The voters of this city are looking for practical answers to urgent questions and will not respond to that kind of _____ and pretentious claptrap.

4. They have a great deal to say on the subject, but unfortunately most of it is meaningless _____.

5. The people trying to "crash" our dance may think of themselves as merry pranksters, but they are really _____ who would prevent us all from having a good time.

6. A good definition of *freedom* is: "The right to do anything you wish as long as you do not _____ on the rights of others."

7. He tries to give the impression of being a true man of the world, but his conduct clearly shows him to be a(n) _____ and somewhat feckless youth.

8. Though fossils show that human beings have been on earth a very, very long time, the earliest written records of their activities date back only about five

_____.

9. This old necklace has little _____ value, but it means a great deal to me because it belonged to my mother.

10. How can we have any respect for people who try to _____ themselves with their superiors by flattery and favors?

11. Throughout the dictator's long reign, some of his most trusted advisors engaged in behind-the-scenes conspiracies and _____ schemes without his knowledge.

12. The Vice President of the United States, the Secretary of State, and the Secretary of Defense are _____ members of the National Security Council.

13. Addressing the school assembly for the first time was a nerve-racking experience, but I managed to deliver my speech with a reasonable amount of _____.

14. That dancer is very talented, but isn't it going rather far to call her "the very _____ of feminine beauty and grace"?

15. We looked up hungrily as the delightful odor of broiled steak and fried onions _____ the room.

16. "The rash and _____ actions of that young hothead almost cost us the battle, to say nothing of the war," the general remarked sourly.

17. We do not know what her motives were, but we may _____ that she was mainly concerned for the child's well-being.

18. Representing an organization of senior citizens, the rally's keynote speaker _____ vehemently against conditions that rob the elderly of their dignity and independence.

19. After completing those long, grueling exams, I was overwhelmed by a(n) _____ so great that I felt I would never be able to study again.

20. "If you think my training rules are too _____ and confining," the coach said, "then you probably shouldn't be a candidate for the team."

Writing: Words in Action

1. Look back at "Why Vote?" (pages 22–23). Suppose you want to persuade the citizens in your community to vote. Write a public service announcement explaining why voting is an important act of citizenship that should be exercised. Use at least two details from the passage and three unit words.

2. *"Those who stay away from the election think that one vote will do no good: 'Tis but one step more to think one vote will do no harm."*—Ralph Waldo Emerson

   Think about Emerson's quotation and why it is important to vote. Write a brief essay in which you describe why each vote is significant to ensure a true democracy. Support your ideas with specific examples from your observations, studies, and the reading (pages 22–23). Write at least three paragraphs, and use three or more words from this unit.

Vocabulary in Context

Literary Text

The following excerpts are from Moby-Dick *by Herman Melville. Some of the words you have studied in this unit appear in **boldface** type. Complete each statement below the excerpt by circling the letter of the correct answer.*

1. But after embattling his facts, an advocate who should wholly suppress a not unreasonable **surmise**, which might tell eloquently upon his cause—such an advocate, would he not be blameworthy?

   To **surmise** something involves

   a. restraining one's emotions
   b. advocating a cause
   c. making deductions
   d. sharing suspicions

2. ...[T]he man who first thus entitled this sort of Ottoman whale, must have read the memoirs of Vidocq, and informed himself what sort of a country-schoolmaster that famous Frenchman was in his younger days, and what was the nature of those **occult** lessons he inculcated into some of his pupils.

   An **occult** lesson is NOT

   a. apparent
   b. ambiguous
   c. veiled
   d. unseen

3. The **precipitating** manner in which Captain Ahab had quitted the Samuel Enderby of London, had not been unattended with some small violence to his own person.

   To depart in a **precipitating** manner involves

   a. refinement
   b. deliberation
   c. great speed
   d. clumsiness

Gregory Peck stars as the obsessed Captain Ahab in the 1956 movie *Moby Dick.*

4. The first time Stubb lowered with him, Pip evinced much nervousness; but happily, for that time, escaped close contact with the whale; and therefore came off not altogether discreditably; though Stubb observing him, took care, afterwards, to **exhort** him to cherish his courageousness to the utmost, for he might often find it needful.

   To **exhort** means to

   a. dissuade
   b. urge
   c. reprimand
   d. soothe

5. ...[A]s the ardour of youth declines...as reflection lends her solemn pauses; in short, as a general **lassitude** overtakes the sated Turk; then a love of ease and virtue supplants the love for maidens....

   Lassitude is a feeling of

   a. youth
   b. vigor
   c. sadness
   d. laziness

Interactive Quiz

Snap the code, or go to **vocabularyworkshop.com**

*Read the following selection, taking note of the **boldface** words and their contexts. These words are among those you will be studying in Unit 3. As you complete the exercises in this unit, it may help to refer to the way the words are used below.*

Trapped in a Cave, Foiled by a Circus

<Journal Entries>

Feb. 2, 1925

Good thing I made a reservation before leaving Chicago, because the hotel here is packed full, and a whole army of people has invaded little Cave City. As I hightailed it over to Sand Cave for an update on the news, I saw some people setting up tents, and others living out of their cars and trucks. Everyone's talking about Floyd Collins. The poor spelunker **inadvertently** became trapped in a cave, and now, after just three days, he's become the biggest sensation since the sinking of the *Titanic!*

I interviewed a town official right away, and he told me Floyd was just a poor Kentucky farmer when he discovered Crystal Caves on his family's land eight years ago. To attract more tourists to the area, Floyd went looking for new caves, and that's when he found Sand Cave. Then his luck gave out, and here we are, waiting for Floyd to come out.

Feb. 3, 1925

Bad news travels fast. There must be tens of thousands of ordinary folk in Cave City today, not to mention the Red Cross and the National Guard, plus hundreds of reporters like me. And let's not forget the stalls set up to feed and entertain all these bystanders! Everyone needs to eat, I suppose, but I suspect at least a few of these "entrepreneurs" don't just sell, but **peculate**, in taking cash from everybody.

William Burke Miller, a young Louisville newspaperman whom everyone calls "Skeets," squeezed down the narrow passageway and made contact with Floyd. Although Skeets was sent to cover the story, his being here is far from **adventitious**, since his small stature allows him access to the cave while the rest of us stand by, feeling useless. He's been bringing food down to Floyd, then interviewing him. People all around the world are now reading his dispatches.

Feb. 4, 1925

Radio reports say that even Congress is getting updates on Floyd! Meanwhile, Skeets keeps bringing down sandwiches, water, and comfort. Floyd remains stuck, so workers are still trying to dig him out. Floyd's **sangfroid** in the midst of this circus is admirable.

Traffic jam outside of Cave City, Kentucky, 1900

Floyd Collins exploring another cave, shortly before his fatal accident in 1925.

Feb. 5, 1925

Interviewed Homer Collins, Floyd's younger brother. "To what do you **ascribe** Floyd's composure in these difficult circumstances?" I asked. Homer: "Well, I reckon Floyd has always been brave in caves, even as a youngster."

Feb. 6, 1925

There are so many journalists here, some will do anything to get a scoop. I've seen a few hardbitten reporters, pretending to be concerned, and kowtowing to locals just to get a quotation for the evening edition; but normally, their prose is so full of **vitriol** that it would make a grown man cry.

Feb. 8, 1925

I **commiserated** with Homer, who is now **enjoined** from helping in the rescue. Others have taken control— they pushed him aside, even though Homer knows more about caving than they do—but their attempts to reach Floyd have failed miserably. The tunnel used to reach Floyd collapsed, so they'll have to dig a **circuitous** route to the trapped man.

Feb. 10, 1925

The collapse of the shaft that had been drilled through the rock has shut Floyd off from the outside.

Floyd Collins

Feb. 11, 1925

I tried to **wheedle** an interview with Miss Jane, Floyd's stepmother. Another reporter got to her first, so I eavesdropped. I didn't catch everything she said, but let's just say she has a **tenuous** hold on reality and a **proclivity** for bending the truth. She seems a bit off in the head, so she is not exactly a reliable source.

Feb. 12, 1925

A few of us quizzed the mayor of Cave City about **expediting** the rescue. So far, all attempts have been **nominal** and feeble. The mayor and his minions are doing their utmost to **ferment** excitement about this crisis and keep the hucksters happy. It sometimes seems as if they are more interested in bringing attention to their town than in rescuing Floyd. It's a sad state of affairs.

Feb. 14, 1925

The new shaft is completed, and rescuers will attempt to reach Floyd. It's been two weeks since he became trapped. Time waits for no man. We need a miracle now.

Feb. 17, 1925

Floyd is dead. I **abominate** what happened here. I witnessed a circus, not a rescue. Some of the participants in this sideshow displayed remorse, but this is a poor way to **expiate** their guilt for the role they played in this travesty. Most of the rest merely shook their heads and walked away.

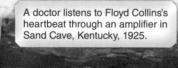

A doctor listens to Floyd Collins's heartbeat through an amplifier in Sand Cave, Kentucky, 1925.

Snap the code, or go to
vocabularyworkshop.com

Definitions

Note the spelling, pronunciation, part(s) of speech, and definition(s) of each of the following words. Then write the word in the blank spaces in the illustrative sentence(s) following. Finally, study the lists of synonyms and antonyms.

1. abominate
(ə bäm' ə nāt)

(*v.*) to have an intense dislike or hatred for

I _____ cruelty yet do not always notice when I have said something inadvertently cruel.

SYNONYMS: loathe, abhor, despise, detest
ANTONYMS: relish, savor, esteem

2. acculturation
(ə kəl chə rā' shən)

(*n.*) the modification of the social patterns, traits, or structures of one group or society by contact with those of another; the resultant blend

Every immigrant group newly arrived in another country goes through a slow process of _____.

SYNONYM: adaptation

3. adventitious
(ad ven tish' əs)

(*adj.*) resulting from chance rather than from an inherent cause or character; accidental, not essential; (medicine) acquired, not congenital

It was no _____ meeting that led to their writing songs together, for in fact they were cousins.

SYNONYMS: extrinsic, incidental, fortuitous
ANTONYMS: essential, intrinsic, inherent, congenital

4. ascribe
(ə skrīb')

(*v.*) to assign or refer to (as a cause or source), attribute

You may _____ these holes to gophers or elves, but I blame the dog from next door.

SYNONYMS: impute, credit

5. circuitous
(sər kyü' ə təs)

(*adj.*) roundabout, not direct

I followed a _____ path through the woods, not because I feared pursuit, but because I was lost.

SYNONYMS: indirect, meandering, winding
ANTONYMS: straight, direct, as the crow flies

6. commiserate
(kə miz' ə rāt)

(*v.*) to sympathize with, have pity or sorrow for, share a feeling of distress

The family _____ with her after the loss of her old and faithful dog.

SYNONYMS: feel sorry for, empathize
ANTONYM: feel no sympathy for

7. enjoin
(en join')

(*v.*) to direct or order; to prescribe a course of action in an authoritative way; to prohibit

I _____ them to stop spending so much money or to face the consequences.

SYNONYMS: bid, charge, adjure; ANTONYMS: allow, permit

8. expedite
(ek' spə dīt)

(*v.*) to make easy, cause to progress faster

The pleasant background music did not _____ my work but instead distracted me.

SYNONYMS: accelerate, facilitate, speed up
ANTONYMS: hinder, hamper, impede, obstruct

9. expiate
(ek' spē āt)

(*v.*) to make amends, make up for; to avert

They seemed more than willing to _____ their guilt by whatever means necessary.

SYNONYMS: redeem, make amends for, make reparation

10. ferment
(*n.*, fər' ment;
v., fər ment')

(*n.*) a state of great excitement, agitation, or turbulence; (*v.*) to be in or work into such a state; to produce alcohol by chemical action

Caught in the _____ of revolution, the young men enlisted with the local militias.

If left for a time, cider will eventually _____.

SYNONYMS: (*n.*) commotion, turmoil, unrest
ANTONYMS: (*n.*) peace and quiet, tranquility, placidity

11. inadvertent
(in əd vər' tənt)

(*adj.*) resulting from or marked by lack of attention; unintentional, accidental

The poor fellow was stronger than he realized, and the damage he did was _____.

SYNONYM: accidental; ANTONYMS: deliberate, intentional

12. nominal
(näm' ə nəl)

(*adj.*) existing in name only, not real; too small to be considered or taken seriously

The new health clinic for lower-income residents charges only _____ fees.

SYNONYMS: titular, inconsequential; ANTONYMS: actual, exorbitant

13. noncommittal
(nän kə mit' əl)

(*adj.*) not decisive or definite; unwilling to take a clear position

We questioned her quietly, carefully, and at length, but her answers remained _____.

SYNONYMS: cagey, uninformative, playing it safe, playing it close to the vest

ANTONYMS: positive, definite, committed

14. **peculate**
(pek′ yü lāt)

(v.) to steal something that has been given into one's trust; to take improperly for one's own use

Investigators discovered that the clerk came up with a scheme to _____ from the company.

SYNONYMS: defraud, misappropriate

15. **proclivity**
(prō kliv′ ə tē)

(n.) a natural or habitual inclination or tendency (especially of human character or behavior)

Curious, patient, and fond of long walks outdoors, she soon displayed a _____ for nature study.

SYNONYMS: penchant, propensity; ANTONYMS: inability, incapacity

16. **sangfroid**
(sän frwä′)

(n.) composure or coolness, especially in trying circumstances

Even when they forget their lines, experienced actors can usually perform with _____.

SYNONYMS: poise, self-assurance, equanimity
ANTONYMS: excitability, hysteria, flappability

17. **seditious**
(sə dish′ əs)

(adj.) resistant to lawful authority; having the purpose of overthrowing an established government

Dictators usually begin their reigns by searching out and silencing _____ opinion.

SYNONYMS: mutinous, rebellious, subversive
ANTONYMS: supportive, faithful, allegiant

18. **tenuous**
(ten′ yü əs)

(adj.) thin, slender, not dense; lacking clarity or sharpness; of slight importance; lacking a sound basis, poorly supported

My grasp of trigonometry was _____ until I attended the remedial study sessions.

SYNONYMS: flimsy, insubstantial, vague, hazy
ANTONYMS: strong, solid, substantial, valid

19. **vitriolic**
(vi trē äl′ ik)

(adj.) bitter, sarcastic; highly caustic or biting (like a strong acid)

Though hurt by his _____ language, I had to admit that some of his points were valid.

SYNONYMS: withering, acerbic, mordant
ANTONYMS: bland, saccharine, honeyed, sugary

20. **wheedle**
(whēd′ əl)

(v.) to use coaxing or flattery to gain some desired end

The spy used charm and flattery in order to _____ the information from the diplomat.

SYNONYMS: inveigle, soft-soap, sweet-talk
ANTONYMS: coerce, browbeat, intimidate, strong-arm

Choosing the Right Word

Select the **boldface** word that better completes each sentence. You might refer to the selection on pages 32–33 to see how most of these words are used in context.

1. It may be an exaggeration to say that American architect Frank Lloyd Wright (**abominated, enjoined**) classical European building designs, but he certainly deviated from them.

2. Peace negotiations between the two countries were already (**circuitous, tenuous**) when the border dispute broke out.

3. Although the Queen or King is the (**nominal, adventitious**) head of state, the Prime Minister is the real leader of the British government.

The Solomon R. Guggenheim Museum in New York was designed by Frank Lloyd Wright.

4. You are following an all too familiar pattern in (**ascribing, expediting**) your failures to everyone except yourself.

5. An experienced politician always tries to avoid making (**fermented, inadvertent**) remarks that may offend some voters.

6. It is only in my fantasies that I display the (**ferment, sangfroid**) associated with movie heroes who are "as cool as a cucumber."

7. I learned that I would have to make a choice between my strong aversion to hard work and my equally strong (**proclivity, wheedle**) for expensive living.

8. Our military is prepared to deal with external aggression, but our best defense against (**sedition, peculation**) at home is the loyalty of the American people.

9. (**Peculation, Sedition**) was a common offense among Roman provincial governors, who, when asked how they made their fortunes, often replied, "In the provinces."

10. The sordid and (**nominal, vitriolic**) language from both candidates is offensive and takes the focus away from the issues.

11. His investments proved to be profitable, but they were (**adventitious, nominal**) rather than the result of knowledge and planning.

12. Modern American society can justly be said to be the end point of the (**commiseration, acculturation**) of diverse groups of immigrants.

13. Although that critic is feared for (**noncommittal, vitriolic**) reviews, I have learned that there is usually a sound basis for her unfavorable judgments.

14. (**Commiseration, Proclivity**) is a noble human emotion, but in itself it is no substitute for vigorous efforts to help other people.

15. Experienced lawyers know that the line between literal truth and slight but significant distortion of the facts is often a (**seditious, tenuous**) one.

16. Her mother (**abominated, acculturated**) laziness of any kind and railed vehemently against sleeping in on Sundays.

17. Even criminals who displayed (**sangfroid, acculturation**) would crack under pressure when confronted by the legendary prosecuting attorney.

18. I was simply unable to follow the (**circuitous, adventitious**) reasoning by which she "proved" that a straight line is not necessarily the shortest distance between two points.

19. With the deadline fast approaching, the local newspaper office was in a (**sedition, ferment**) of last-minute activity and preparation.

20. The worst way I can think of to (**expedite, ascribe**) this program would be to set up another new Committee on New Programs.

21. Because he has been able to (**expiate, wheedle**) almost anything he wants out of his parents, he is quite unprepared now to face the harsh realities of life.

22. They are conscientious objectors to military service because they are (**enjoined, ascribed**) by a deep personal conviction not to take a human life.

23. After he had seen the error of his ways, the villain attempted to (**expiate, enjoin**) the dark deeds of his past by acts of kindness and mercy.

24. When I spoke to Mother about going on the spring trip to Washington, her only reply was a (**nominal, noncommittal**) "We'll see."

25. This is a (**nominal, circuitous**) route, but we avoid the traffic jams on the Interstate.

Synonyms

*Choose the word from this unit that is the same or most nearly the same in meaning as the **boldface** word or expression in the phrase. Write that word on the line. Use a dictionary if necessary.*

1. **vacillating** in her answer _____

2. mail that needs to be **rushed** _____

3. an **unplanned** meeting _____

4. **embezzle** from the treasury _____

5. was **cajoled** into agreeing _____

6. a **rancorous** tone of voice _____

7. the **assimilation** of American students in Spain _____

8. to **atone** for her unkindness _____

9. a **treasonable** act _____

10. **identify with** your disappointment _____

Antonyms

*Choose the word from this unit that is most nearly opposite in meaning to the **boldface** word or expression in the phrase. Write that word on the line. Use a dictionary if necessary.*

1. **cherish** everything about her   _____

2. a **calculated** misuse of the money   _____

3. a **clear-cut** statement of intentions   _____

4. a kingdom filled with **loyal** subjects   _____

5. evidenced by **nonconformity**   _____

Completing the Sentence

From the words in this unit, choose the one that best completes each of the following sentences. Write the word in the space provided.

1. You could have indicated frankly what you thought was wrong without embittering them with such _____ criticism.

2. His line of questioning was so _____ that I began to suspect that he was not sure of what he was trying to prove.

3. Only someone who has suffered from bursitis can fully _____ with me when I am in the throes of an acute attack.

4. He _____ the crime committed during his youth by a lifetime of service to humanity.

5. If, as you say, your slamming of the door on the way out was completely _____, then you should be more careful in the future.

6. Much of the money that the "robber barons" _____ from the public trust was never recovered—or even missed!

7. Wines from that part of France are produced by _____ the juice of the luscious grapes that grow on the hillsides.

8. We had hoped to learn his opinion of the new energy program, but he remained completely _____ during the interview.

9. He claims to be a close friend of the Senator, but I believe that the connection between them is extremely _____.

10. Who in the world can hope to match the unshakable _____ of the indestructible James Bond in moments of great peril?

11. No matter what their other likes or dislikes are, most Americans thoroughly
_____ slavery in all its forms.

12. We must distinguish between the truly basic policies of our political party and
those that are _____ and have little connection with the
essential program.

13. Certain languages such as Afrikaans are the product of _____
and were created when two societies merged.

14. Since she seems to have a strong _____ both for science and
for service to others, I think that she should plan to study medicine.

15. As charming, clever, and persuasive as you may be, you will certainly not
_____ me into lending you my tennis racquet.

16. We Americans do not believe that honest criticism of our public officials, no matter
how severe, should be regarded as _____.

17. Declaring the boycott to be illegal, the judge _____ the labor
union from striking against the employing firm.

18. Some people say that they cannot understand her defeat in the election, but I
_____ it to her failure to discuss the issues in simple, down-to-
earth terms.

19. While he remained the _____ leader of the group, the real power
passed into the hands of his wily aide.

20. The new computerized referral system will greatly _____ the
processing of complaints by customers.

Writing: Words in Action

1. Look back at "Trapped in a Cave, Foiled by a Circus" (pages 32–33). Imagine
that you are a journalist who has been sent to Cave City to cover this event.
Write a short article describing the scene and the mood of those around you.
Use at least two details from the passage and three unit words.

2. Many people take risks pursuing their dreams, yet there is a difference
between taking risks and being reckless. Without risk-takers, humanity would
not have explored new frontiers, created advanced technology, or walked on
the moon. Reckless behavior, on the other hand, often leads to disaster. Write
a brief essay in which you compare risk-takers to those who act recklessly.
Support your ideas with specific examples from your observations, studies,
and the reading (pages 32–33). Write at least three paragraphs, and use three
or more words from this unit.

Vocabulary in Context

Literary Text

The following excerpts are from The Writings of Thomas Jefferson *and* Memoirs, Correspondence, and Miscellanies *by Thomas Jefferson. Some of the words you have studied in this unit appear in* **boldface** *type. Complete each statement below the excerpt by circling the letter of the correct answer.*

1. I congratulate you, my dear friend, on the law of your State, for suspending the importation of slaves, and for the glory you have justly acquired by endeavoring to prevent it forever. This **abomination** must have an end. (*Writings*)

An **abomination** is a(n)

a. atrocity
b. organization
c. lifestyle
d. dilemma

2. SIR,—A dislocation of my right wrist has for upwards of three months prevented my writing to you. I begin to use it a little for the pen; but it is with great pain. To this cause alone I hope you will **ascribe** that I have acknowledged at one time the receipt of so many of your letters. (*Writings*)

To **ascribe** means to

a. publish
b. forgive
c. accredit
d. conceal

3. To save time, I wrote to Mr. Dumas, to know whether he thought it probable a loan could be obtained, **enjoining** on him the strictest secrecy, and informing him I was making the inquiry merely of my own motion, and without instruction. (*Writings*)

The act of **enjoining** involves

a. uniting
b. ranking
c. consenting
d. commanding

The Jefferson Memorial commemorates the third President of the United States.

4. With respect to what they call the reduction of the debt from its **nominal** sum, it is not a reduction of it, but an appreciation at its true value. (*Writings*)

A **nominal** sum is one that is

a. popular
b. easy
c. trifling
d. significant

5. That the resolution . . . for suppressing the exercise of all powers derived from the crown, had shown, by the **ferment** into which it had thrown these middle colonies, that they had not yet accommodated their minds to a separation from the mother country. . . . (*Memoirs, Correspondence, and Miscellanies*)

A **ferment** does NOT entail

a. chaos
b. stability
c. disorder
d. education

Interactive Quiz

Snap the code, or go to
vocabularyworkshop.com

Vocabulary for Comprehension

*Read the following selection in which some of the words you have studied in Units 1–3 appear in **boldface** type. Then answer the questions on page 43.*

Douglas Corrigan, the legendary pilot who is the subject of this passage, gained celebrity in an unconventional way.

(Line)

Readers of American history know that in 1927 Charles A. Lindbergh made the first solo flight across the Atlantic Ocean in a plane called the

(5) *Spirit of St. Louis.* But how many people know that in 1938 Douglas Corrigan achieved what might be called the first trans-Atlantic hoax?

At 31, Corrigan, a native Texan,

(10) was an airplane mechanic and flight instructor who longed to fly across the Atlantic. To **assuage** this itch, he prepared his 1929 Curtis-Robin monoplane for the journey; but

(15) because of its age and poor condition, federal aviation authorities refused to certify the plane for a transoceanic flight. Even so, Corrigan flew his patched-up plane

(20) from California to New York in the summer of 1938. He then **elicited** permission from the aviation authorities to fly back home to California. Like Lindbergh, Corrigan

(25) took off from Long Island. Since his flight plan showed a return trip to California, his departure **precipitated** no suspicion. As he took off, he must have seemed the

(30) very **epitome** of an innocent amateur, for the flight staff at the Long Island airfield noted that he headed eastward into clouds instead of turning west. This seemed a

(35) **circuitous** way to begin a trip to Los Angeles!

Twenty-eight hours and thirteen minutes later, an odd-looking plane landed at an airfield in Dublin,

(40) Ireland. "I'm Douglas Corrigan," said the pilot. "Just got in from New York. Where am I?" (The outrage of the American officials, when they heard, can be imagined; but Corrigan

(45) continued to play the part of a cheerful, well-meaning amateur.) He **ascribed** his "mistake" in direction to a remarkably faulty compass and said that the clouds below him had

(50) kept him from seeing that he was flying over an ocean rather than the continental United States.

Within hours of his landing, the story of "Wrong Way" Corrigan

(55) circled the world. Though his flight license was suspended for a short time, he was given a ticker-tape parade upon his return to New York. During a time of economic

(60) depression, Corrigan, who thwarted authority with a grin and a wink, captured Americans' hearts. He stuck by his story—that he had gotten lost on his way to California—

(65) for the rest of his life.

1. The primary purpose of the passage is to
   a. review Corrigan's training for a historic flight
   b. describe Corrigan's monoplane
   c. focus on Corrigan's regret for a mistake
   d. compare Corrigan with Charles Lindbergh
   e. explain how Corrigan earned the sobriquet "Wrong Way"

2. The authorities denied Corrigan permission to make a transoceanic flight because
   a. his actions seemed suspicious
   b. he filed his application too late
   c. he could not pay the required fees
   d. his plane was old and in poor condition
   e. the poor weather made flying dangerous

3. The meaning of **assuage** (line 12) is
   a. allay
   b. pay for
   c. begin
   d. aggravate
   e. increase

4. **Elicited** (line 21) most nearly means
   a. ignored
   b. extracted
   c. falsified
   d. inferred
   e. pleaded for

5. **Precipitated** (line 28) is best defined as
   a. rained
   b. suggested
   c. provoked
   d. got rid of
   e. hurled down

6. In lines 29–36, the author suggests that the flight staff
   a. used a faulty compass
   b. were confused by the poor weather
   c. cooperated with Corrigan in his hoax
   d. mistook Corrigan for an amateur
   e. were told that Corrigan would take off heading eastward

7. The meaning of **epitome** (line 30) is
   a. inspiration
   b. imitation
   c. picture
   d. opposite
   e. model

8. **Circuitous** (line 35) most nearly means
   a. indirect
   b. silly
   c. mysterious
   d. dangerous
   e. direct

9. **Ascribed** (line 47) is best defined as
   a. restricted
   b. described
   c. attributed
   d. concealed
   e. denied

10. The passage implies that none of the following feelings inspired the nickname "Wrong Way" Corrigan EXCEPT
    a. disillusionment
    b. affectionate approval
    c. envy
    d. greed
    e. popular outrage

11. For the most part, which of the following organizational methods does the writer use?
    a. spatial order
    b. cause and effect
    c. chronological order
    d. comparison and contrast
    e. order of importance

12. The author's attitude toward Corrigan is best described as one of
    a. admiration
    b. hostility
    c. indifference
    d. embarrassment
    e. annoyance

Two-Word Completions

Select the pair of words that best complete the meaning of each of the following passages.

1. While the Roman people remained vigorous and aggressive, their empire flourished. Once they began to sink into a sort of physical and spiritual _____, however, the empire became feeble and _____.
   a. umbrage . . . petulant
   b. lassitude . . . decadent
   c. aplomb . . . jaded
   d. ferment . . . adventitious

2. "The general's death-defying feats of gallantry in the recent war certainly deserve our _____," the article declared. "But, by the same token, his wanton acts of cruelty _____ our severest censure."
   a. umbrage . . . enjoin
   b. approbation . . . merit
   c. aplomb . . . expiate
   d. sangfroid . . . elicit

3. "A(n) _____ government will prove workable only as long as its members are able to _____ party differences," the professor remarked. "As soon as they become entangled in factional disputes, the partnership will begin to collapse."
   a. provincial . . . surmise
   b. ex officio . . . abominate
   c. seditious . . . ameliorate
   d. coalition . . . transcend

4. Though my teaching job entails numerous responsibilities, it also brings with it certain _____, one of which is the right to use school equipment, services, and facilities during the _____ between semesters or the summer break.
   a. prerogatives . . . hiatus
   b. surmises . . . innuendoes
   c. simulations . . . millennia
   d. ameliorations . . . proclivities

5. Some Senators favored the new budget proposal and in the warmest terms _____ their colleagues to pass the measure. Others disliked the idea and just as vehemently _____ against its adoption.
   a. wheedled . . . enjoined
   b. assuaged . . . interceded
   c. exhorted . . . inveighed
   d. elicited . . . infringed

6. Though the Prime Minister actually directs the British government, the reigning monarch is the _____ head of state and, by virtue of that position, also the _____ leader of the Anglican Church.
   a. intrinsic . . . occult
   b. tenuous . . . inadvertent
   c. nominal . . . ex officio
   d. adventitious . . . noncommittal

7. As a result of the recent actions of several _____, who have since been indicted, the bank has instituted a new set of _____ guidelines regarding the transfer of funds.
   a. interlopers . . . hackneyed
   b. coalitions . . . lurid
   c. peculators . . . stringent
   d. provincials . . . ingratiating

Idioms

In the essay "Why Vote?" (see pages 22–23), the author talks about autocrats who "pay lip service to" democratic ideals. What the writer means is that the autocrats talk about the importance of democratic ideals, but they do not put these ideals into practice.

The phrase "pay lip service to" is an **idiom**—an expression that is not meant to be taken literally. Like other types of figurative language, idioms ask the reader or listener to associate two unlike things and create a mental image. Even if you have never heard a particular idiom before, you may be able to determine its meaning from its imagery or from the surrounding context. Some idioms, however, defy easy interpretation and must simply be memorized.

Choosing the Right Idiom

Read each sentence. Use context clues to figure out the meaning of each idiom in ***boldface*** *print. Then write the letter of the definition for the idiom in the sentence.*

1. Of course I will not tell a soul how much you spent on those jeans. **My lips are sealed**! _____

2. My trainer has a **bee in her bonnet** about sugar, and she advises against drinking soda or eating foods that are sweetened. _____

3. You can count on Jonas to **go the extra mile** and produce a spectacular play. _____

4. Renee has been **pounding the pavement** every day, but she still cannot find a job. _____

5. You can tell by the intricate details in the carving that Marco put a lot of **blood**, **sweat**, **and tears** into building his boat. _____

6. Quit **dragging your feet** and decide which college you want to attend. _____

7. It is so typical of Mandy to **pass the buck** and assign her work to other members in the group. _____

8. Chad got a job at the bank during a hiring freeze because his father, a high-level manager, **pulled strings**. _____

9. Though many politicians enjoy **sitting on the fence**, this election will require candidates to be more committed. _____

10. Anna has **burned so many bridges**, I'm surprised anyone in this town wants to hire her. _____

a. tremendous hard work and effort

b. do more than is expected

c. used political or personal influence to obtain something

d. a promise to maintain a secret

e. refusing to take sides on an issue

f. postponing or delaying a decision or action

g. alienated or destroyed prior relationships

h. an idea that occupies one's thoughts; an obsession

i. diligently seeking something, such as a job

j. avoid responsibility by giving it to others

Writing with Idioms

Find the meaning of each idiom. (Use an online or print dictionary if necessary.) Then write a sentence for each idiom.

1. out of the blue

_____

2. step out of line

_____

3. throw someone a bone

_____

4. get over it

_____

5. dot all the *i*'s and cross all the *t*'s

_____

_____

6. bend over backwards

_____

_____

7. deep pockets

_____

_____

8. down to the wire

_____

9. in the dark

_____

10. snowed under

_____

11. tickled pink

_____

12. hit the ground running

_____

Denotation and Connotation

A dictionary provides the **denotation** of a word—its objective, neutral meaning. Many words, however, carry emotional associations that suggest an additional layer of meaning. This emotional association, or **connotation,** can be positive or negative.

Imagine that your best friend enters the classroom. Was your friend *walking, sashaying, striding, ambling, shuffling,* or *trudging*? Although these words have similar denotations (they all describe a walking movement), each one has a different connotation.

Consider these synonyms for the word *exhort.*

> *appeal   beseech   compel   demand*

Appeal and *beseech* suggest a plea or request being made by a person in a lower position to a person in a higher, more powerful position. *Compel* and *demand* suggest someone in a position of power making a forceful request.

> **Think:** A lord may *appeal to* or *beseech* the king to grant him a favor, but a king can *compel* or *demand* his subjects to follow his orders.

Look at these examples of words. Notice how the connotation of each word varies.

NEUTRAL	POSITIVE	NEGATIVE
talkative	conversational	bombastic
composure	sangfroid	coldness
argue	expostulate	complain

Writers choose their words based on the mood they wish to convey. If a writer wishes to convey a peaceful mood, she may write about waves *lapping* on the shore. If she wants to create a more dramatic mood, she might write about waves *crashing* along the shore. By understanding the emotional power of words, writers can better reach their audience.

Shades of Meaning

Write a plus sign (+) in the box if the word has a positive connotation.
Write a minus sign (–) if the word has a negative connotation. Put a zero (0)
if the word is neutral.

1. assuage ☐   **2.** coalition ☐   **3.** lurid ☐   **4.** sangfroid ☐

5. infringe ☐   **6.** aplomb ☐   **7.** interloper ☐   **8.** unctuous ☐

9. abominate ☐   **10.** jaded ☐   **11.** ascribe ☐   **12.** expiate ☐

13. precipitate ☐   **14.** ameliorate ☐   **15.** proclivity ☐   **16.** seditious ☐

Expressing the Connotation

Read each sentence. Select the word in parentheses that expresses the connotation (positive, negative, or neutral) given at the beginning of the sentence.

positive
1. Upon receiving a (**meritorious, satisfactory**) review, Andrea rose to a managerial position in the company.

neutral
2. Many people associate the ancient Romans with a lifestyle of (**decadence, excess**).

neutral
3. It is natural for (**callow, inexperienced**) people to assume they have all the answers.

positive
4. Her acceptance speech, in which she thanked all those who had helped her, was the (**epitome, model**) of graciousness and modesty.

negative
5. I don't know how you can listen to your brother's constant (**talk, drivel**) about car engines.

positive
6. Amid the student (**excitement, ferment**), it was difficult to hear Principal Gooden announce which school had won the award.

negative
7. Sometimes it is difficult for people to differentiate between (**vitriolic, unkind**) rhetoric and political discourse.

negative
8. That famous sculptor, known to be (**difficult, petulant**), seldom attends his own openings and shuns public appearances.

Challenge: Using Connotation

Choose vocabulary words from Units 1–3 to replace the highlighted words in the sentences below. Then explain how the connotation of the replacement word changes the tone of the sentence.

approbation	stringent	nominal
circuitous	innuendo	provincial

1. When Eric arrived an hour late, he ignored Nina's **hint** _____ about his habitual tardiness.

   _____
   _____

2. It is obvious that your spending is out of control, so you will now be put on a **sensible** _____ budget.

   _____
   _____

3. I seldom like to dine out with my brother, as his **unsophisticated** _____ manners are an embarrassment to me.

   _____
   _____

Classical Roots

cede, cess, ceas—to happen, yield, go

The root *cede* appears in **intercede** (page 15). The literal meaning is "to go between," but the word now means "to ask a favor from one person for another." Some other words based on the same root are listed below.

accede	cessation	decease	predecessor
accessory	concession	precedence	recession

From the list of words above, choose the one that corresponds to each of the brief definitions below. Write the word in the blank space in the illustrative sentence below the definition. Use an online or print dictionary if necessary.

1. a withdrawal, departure; a period of economic slump

Millions of workers were unemployed during the _____.

2. to give in, agree; to attain (*"to yield to"*)

The king's subjects are expected to _____ to all his requests.

3. death (*"going away"*)

Marcia will inherit the estate after her aunt's _____.

4. an admission, anything yielded, a compromise; a franchise

There is always a line at the food _____.

5. someone or something that comes before another in time, especially in an office or position (*"one who leaves before"*)

Starting today, I will take over from my _____.

6. a stopping, ceasing

The ambassador called for a(n) _____ of hostilities.

7. priority in order, rank, or importance

Studying for finals must take _____ over everything else.

8. something added, a finishing touch; a helper in a crime

Her sister was held by the police as a(n) _____.

*Read the following selection, taking note of the **boldface** words and their contexts. These words are among those you will be studying in Unit 4. As you complete the exercises in this unit, it may help to refer to the way the words are used below.*

Ada Byron: Visionary Mathematician

<Biographical Sketch>

Ada Byron was born in London, England, in 1815, the daughter of the famed poet Lord Byron and his wife, Anna Milbanke. Ada's parents separated months after she was born. She never knew her father, who left England in 1816 and died when Ada was only nine years old. By the time they separated, Anna Milbanke had a thoroughly negative view of Lord Byron, believing him to be an unfaithful and **scurrilous** man. She feared that Ada might inherit the wild poetic **propensities** of her father, and she hoped that rigorous training in mathematics would discourage the development of unruly tendencies in her daughter. Thus, Ada spent much of her early life in the intelligent **aura** of **erudite** tutors, including some of the most brilliant mathematical minds of her day.

Ada was a **sedulous** student who excelled in mathematics, and she grew to become a talented and insightful mathematician. But the apple doesn't fall far from the tree. Ada's fretful mother was **querulous** about her daughter's poetic tendencies and **remonstrated** with her about their dangers, but Ada refused to **repudiate** her poetic qualities. And so Ada Byron became a gifted mathematician with a vivid imagination and a flair for language. She proved especially skillful at expressing mathematical concepts in writing. Though she suffered from illnesses throughout her life, she had a **resilient** spirit and remained focused on her studies and her rich social life.

When Ada was only seventeen years old, she met Charles Babbage. Babbage was a professor of mathematics who was designing an "analytical engine," a mechanical computing machine that was an **archetype** of the modern computer. Ada was fascinated by Babbage's description of the machine. She corresponded with him for the rest of her life, discussing mathematics, logic, and the operation of the analytical engine. In 1842, when an article about Babbage's

Ada Byron

machine was published in French, he asked Ada to translate it into English and to add her own explanatory notes to the English translation.

Babbage was not an **affable** man. He often **aggrandized** his own accomplishments and neglected to give credit to others. But he was so impressed with Ada's work that he conceded she might have understood his machine even better than he did, and that she was "far, far better at explaining it." Many mathematicians of the day had only an imperfect understanding of Babbage's machine, considering it an **inscrutable** and impractical device. Ada's notes provided a clear explanation for her contemporaries and included descriptions of procedures that are today considered to be the first computer programs. In addition, Ada imagined applications of the machine that went beyond the **insular** field of mathematics. She foresaw that it could be used to compose music and could be put to a wide range of other symbolic uses.

Charles Babbage may have been the first person to design a computer, but Ada Byron was the first person to recognize the full potential of his machine. Especially remarkable in an age in which women were discouraged from participating in mathematics and the sciences, Ada's profound mathematical understanding, her eloquence in explaining the operation of Babbage's analytical engine, and her visionary insight into its many uses are accomplishments that continue to **reverberate** throughout history.

Charles Babbage

Snap the code, or go to **vocabularyworkshop.com**

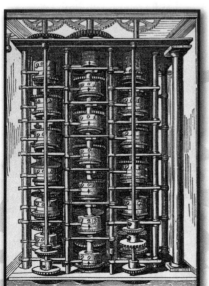

Charles Babbage designed a calculating machine called the Difference Engine before designing the analytical engine.

Procedures like those described by Ada Byron are performed by computer processors today.

Definitions

Note the spelling, pronunciation, part(s) of speech, and definition(s) of each of the following words. Then write the word in the blank spaces in the illustrative sentence(s) following. Finally, study the lists of synonyms and antonyms.

1. affable
(af′ ə bəl)

(*adj.*) courteous and pleasant, sociable, easy to speak to

We spent a pleasant afternoon with our _____ neighbors.

SYNONYMS: genial, amicable, cordial
ANTONYMS: surly, cantankerous, dour, inhospitable

2. aggrandize
(ə gran′ dīz)

(*v.*) to increase in greatness, power, or wealth; to build up or intensify; to make appear greater

John D. Rockefeller worked to _____ his empire by purchasing oil wells, refineries, and pipelines.

SYNONYMS: augment, amplify, enhance, exalt
ANTONYMS: reduce, decrease, diminish

3. amorphous
(ə môr′ fəs)

(*adj.*) shapeless, without definite form; of no particular type or character; without organization, unity, or cohesion

The _____ body of the amoeba was fascinating to watch under the microscope.

SYNONYMS: formless, unstructured, inchoate
ANTONYMS: definite, well-defined, clear-cut

4. archetype
(är′ kə tīp)

(*n.*) an original model on which something was patterned or replicated; the ideal example of a particular type of person or thing

Sherlock Holmes was an _____ of a clever detective who always solves the case.

SYNONYMS: model, prototype, epitome

5. aura
(ôr′ ə)

(*n.*) that which surrounds (as an atmosphere); a distinctive air or personal quality

What people thought was her _____ of mystery was actually a mask for her shyness.

SYNONYMS: ambience, atmosphere

6. contraband
(kän′ trə band)

(*n.*) illegal traffic, smuggled goods; (*adj.*) illegal, prohibited

Three jeweled combs from the 17ᵗʰ century were among the _____ seized by the police.

SYNONYMS: (*adj.*) bootleg, unlawful
ANTONYMS: (*adj.*) legal, lawful, licit

7. erudite
(er′ yü dīt)

(*adj.*) scholarly, learned, bookish, pedantic
For my paper, I would like to find an _____ history of the subject written in a clear and unbiased manner.
SYNONYMS: profoundly educated, well-read
ANTONYMS: ignorant, uneducated, illiterate

8. gossamer
(gäs′ ə mər)

(*adj.*) thin, light, delicate, insubstantial; (*n.*) a very thin, light cloth
Ghosts are often depicted in literature as wearing _____ clothing that makes them seem all the more ethereal.
The book was so old that each finely printed page seemed only the weight of _____.
SYNONYMS: (*adj.*) filmy, diaphanous, sheer, airy, feathery, gauzy
ANTONYMS: (*adj.*) dense, solid, massive

9. inscrutable
(in skrü′ tə bəl)

(*adj.*) incapable of being understood; impossible to see through physically
I could not tell by her _____ smile whether she was pleased or only amused with me.
SYNONYMS: impenetrable, incomprehensible, enigmatic
ANTONYMS: comprehensible, intelligible, penetrable

10. insular
(in′ syə lər)

(*adj.*) relating to, characteristic of, or situated on an island; narrow or isolated in outlook or experience
You seem too sophisticated to hold such _____ opinions.
SYNONYMS: narrow-minded, parochial, provincial
ANTONYMS: catholic, cosmopolitan, liberal

11. irrevocable
(i rev′ ə kə bəl)

(*adj.*) incapable of being changed or called back
We tend to think of court verdicts as _____, but they are often overturned by higher courts.
SYNONYMS: unrecallable, unalterable
ANTONYMS: reversible, changeable

12. propensity
(prə pen′ sə tē)

(*n.*) a natural inclination or predilection toward
Queen Elizabeth I showed a strong _____ for putting off decisions in the hopes that they would resolve themselves.
SYNONYMS: natural bent, proclivity, penchant
ANTONYMS: natural incapacity or inability

13. querulous
(kwer′ ə ləs)

(*adj.*) peevish, complaining, fretful
Some flight attendants dread a _____ airline passenger more than they do rough weather.
SYNONYMS: petulant, irritable; ANTONYMS: uncomplaining, stoical

14. remonstrate
(ri män′ strāt)

(*v.*) to argue with someone against something, protest against
Slowly, carefully, keeping his voice down, he argued with the caller as one might _____ with a child.
SYNONYMS: reason against, expostulate

15. repudiate
(ri pyü′ dē āt)

(*v.*) to disown, reject, or deny the validity of
He was forced to _____ a statement he had made before he'd had all the information.
SYNONYMS: disavow, renounce; ANTONYMS: avow, affirm, aver

16. resilient
(ri zil′ yənt)

(*adj.*) able to return to an original shape or form; able to recover quickly
The development of lightweight, _____ plastics revolutionized the design of many durable goods.
SYNONYMS: springy, elastic; ANTONYMS: rigid, stiff, inflexible

17. reverberate
(ri vər′ bə rāt)

(*v.*) to re-echo, resound; to reflect or be reflected repeatedly
From the construction site, the noise of bulldozers and dump trucks _____ across the valley.
SYNONYMS: rumble, thunder, boom, echo

18. scurrilous
(skər′ ə ləs)

(*adj.*) coarsely abusive, vulgar or low (especially in language), foul-mouthed
Days passed and unrest grew, and soon the rebels began a _____ attack on their absent leader.
SYNONYMS: obscene, filthy, abusive, vituperative
ANTONYMS: decorous, seemly, tasteful, dignified

19. sedulous
(sej′ ə ləs)

(*adj.*) persistent, showing industry and determination
No one could say that he was lazy, for he was a careful, _____ copier of other people's work.
SYNONYMS: assiduous, indefatigable; ANTONYMS: indolent, listless

20. sleazy
(slē′ zē)

(*adj.*) thin or flimsy in texture; cheap; shoddy or inferior in quality or character; ethically low, mean, or disreputable
My grandmother made her clothes at home in order to avoid the _____ goods sold in the general store.
SYNONYMS: inferior, cheesy; ANTONYMS: superior, first-rate

Choosing the Right Word

*Select the **boldface** word that better completes each sentence. You might refer to the selection on pages 50–51 to see how most of these words are used in context.*

1. I think that nothing in Shakespeare is lighter or more delightful than the (**gossamer, aggrandized**) wit and fancy of *A Midsummer Night's Dream.*

2. Our determination never to yield to force or the threat of force is firm and (**amorphous, irrevocable**)!

3. Lucy finally completed her (**querulous, erudite**) term paper, in which she quoted from more than a hundred sources.

4. In an age when the world has become a "global village," we cannot afford leaders with (**insular, sedulous**) outlooks.

5. After compiling feedback on the aircraft's design, the engineering group gathered to make improvements to the (**propensity, archetype**).

In *A Midsummer Night's Dream,* fairies intervene in the lives of four young lovers.

6. We cannot bar foreign influences from our shores, and we cannot treat unfamiliar ideas as (**aura, contraband**)!

7. The musical composition, with no melodic pattern and no well-defined structure of development, seemed (**amorphous, querulous**) to my ear.

8. I tried to make some sense out of the strange orders he had given us, but his plan and purpose remained utterly (**erudite, inscrutable**).

9. Surrounded by people who voiced dismal ideas about the economy, Heather found their (**erudite, insular**) views disquieting.

10. The language he used in his bitter attack on us was so (**amorphous, scurrilous**) that I hesitate even to repeat it.

11. What we really resent is not sensible criticism but nagging that is petty, capricious, and (**querulous, affable**).

12. The philosopher said that the ancient question "Am I my brother's keeper?" has continued to (**reverberate, aggrandize**) through the ages.

13. Since he seems to have no moral standards whatsoever, it would probably be futile to (**reverberate, remonstrate**) with him about his outrageous behavior.

14. To keep the mosquitoes from biting us while we slept, we hung lightweight, (**sedulous, gossamer**) mosquito netting around our cots.

15. Your (**propensity, repudiation**) for spending more than you can afford will lead to only one result—bankruptcy!

16. The pitiful derelict's only protection against the elements was a cheap overcoat made out of some kind of (**resilient, sleazy**) material that wouldn't keep the cold out in a heat wave.

17. Throughout his career, the man has emphasized the (**aggrandizement, inscrutability**) of wealth and power at the expense of other values.

18. The four-year-old twins, Martin and Harrison, are such (**affable, querulous**) children that babysitting for them is a pleasure.

19. The concert was held in an outdoor amphitheater, causing the sounds to (**reverberate, repudiate**) throughout the canyon.

20. Carefully avoiding any attempt at originality, he has fashioned his style on (**sedulous, scurrilous**) mimicry of other, more talented writers.

21. On its centennial, the entire country was immersed in a(n) (**propensity, aura**) of patriotism that was difficult to convey to outsiders.

22. When we arrived home, we were tired and depressed, but the (**gossamer, resilient**) spirit of youth made things look brighter the next morning.

23. To limit the free expression of unpopular ideas is to (**repudiate, aggrandize**) the basic spirit of the Bill of Rights.

24. While searching the ship's cargo, inspectors discovered a secret compartment containing (**resilient, contraband**) animals, including several endangered species.

25. What a pleasure to talk about old times with so (**affable, erudite**) a companion!

Synonyms

*Choose the word from this unit that is the same or most nearly the same in meaning as the **boldface** word or expression in the phrase. Write that word on the line. Use a dictionary if necessary.*

1. **ethereal** wings of a dragonfly _____

2. had a festive **feeling** _____

3. said her decision was **irreversible** _____

4. a **tawdry** appearance _____

5. answer with an **unreadable** smile _____

6. only a **nebulous** idea of his future _____

7. **disclaim** an earlier promise _____

8. a relaxed, **agreeable** companion _____

9. thieves smuggling **illicit** materials _____

10. **academic** study of the topic _____

Antonyms

*Choose the word from this unit that is most nearly opposite in meaning to the **boldface** word or expression in the phrase. Write that word on the line. Use a dictionary if necessary.*

1. sturdy discarded items in the resale bin _____

2. known for their **distinctive** style _____

3. all **officially permitted** items should be claimed _____

4. a **variable** clause in the contract _____

5. a **thick** morning mist on the garden _____

Completing the Sentence

From the words in this unit, choose the one that best completes each of the following sentences. Write the word in the space provided.

1. While tsarist Russia's vast territories were almost purely continental, the British Empire included numerous _____ possessions.

2. The drops of dew sparkled like diamonds on the _____ threads of the spider web.

3. Perhaps she had less native ability than some of her classmates, but her powers of concentration and _____ study program enabled her to finish first in the class.

4. On his combat uniform, he wore absolutely no insignia of rank, but he was surrounded with an unmistakable _____ of authority.

5. As my opponent cited facts and figures without once referring to notes, I became aware of how _____ she was.

6. If you happen to have a(n) _____ seatmate on a long airplane flight, you may find yourself talking more freely about personal matters than you would under other circumstances.

7. The program he suggested was so barren of guiding ideas and specific proposals that I felt justified in referring to it as _____.

8. When asked to create a science fiction villain for a story, many writers refer to Frankenstein, the _____ of a mad doctor.

9. Since our efforts to _____ with the factory managers about pollution of the lake have been ineffective, we are now considering legal action.

10. The sharp crack of the rifle shot _____ through the hills.

11. _____ dives full of disreputable and dangerous-looking characters have given the waterfront areas of many cities a bad reputation.

12. He tried in vain to guess what surprise he might expect next from that _____ power, Lady Luck.

13. Because of his _____ for gossiping, we tried not to let him learn anything about our personal affairs.

14. This jacket is made of a material so _____ that it sheds wrinkles and keeps its shape even when one has worn it for days.

15. His attempts to discredit her by belittling her ability and character were nothing more than _____ abuse.

16. He used his admittedly remarkable talents only to _____ himself, not to benefit the society that was so kind to him.

17. Under the latest regulations, any shipment of arms to those countries is illegal and may be seized as _____.

18. I am not going to _____ the ideas and standards by which I have guided my life just because they have become unpopular.

19. The commitment you have made is _____ without the consent of the other party to the agreement.

20. He is really insufferable when he gets into one of those _____ moods in which nothing in the world pleases him.

Writing: Words in Action

1. Look back at "Ada Byron: Visionary Mathematician" (pages 50–51). Suppose you had the opportunity to write to Babbage about computers in the twenty-first century. Follow in Ada Byron's footsteps and compose a short letter to Babbage, explaining how computers are used today. Use at least two details from the passage and three unit words.

2. Technology has developed rapidly over the past thirty years and has made significant changes in the way people live. Think about the many ways in which technology has changed our lives, and then write a brief essay in which you describe one of these changes. Include your opinion as to whether the change has helped or hindered society. Support your ideas with specific examples, observations, and the reading (pages 50–51). Write at least three paragraphs, and use three or more words from this unit.

Vocabulary in Context

Literary Text

The following excerpts are from The Scarlet Letter *by Nathaniel Hawthorne. Some of the words you have studied in this unit appear in **boldface** type. Complete each statement below the excerpt by circling the letter of the correct answer.*

1. "It was found," said the Sexton, "this morning on the scaffold where evil-doers are set up to public shame. Satan dropped it there, I take it, intending a **scurrilous** jest against your reverence."

   An action taken in a **scurrilous** manner is

   a. antiquated   **c.** abusive
   b. mischievous   **d.** mysterious

2. ...[H]e had made the manner of his death a parable, in order to impress on his admirers the mighty and mournful lesson, that...we are sinners all alike. It was to teach them, that the holiest amongst us has but attained so far above his fellows as to discern more clearly the Mercy which looks down, and **repudiate** more utterly the phantom of human merit, which would look aspiringly upward.

   To **repudiate** something means to

   a. protect it   **c.** give in
   b. forsake it   **d.** think over

Demi Moore plays Hester Prynne in the 1995 film adaptation of *The Scarlet Letter.*

3. Then, it is true, the **propensity** of human nature to tell the very worst of itself, when embodied in the person of another, would constrain them to whisper the black scandal of bygone years.

   A **propensity** is a(n)

   a. imitation   **c.** tendency
   b. aversion   **d.** sensation

4. Pearl mumbled something into his ear that...was only such gibberish as children may be heard amusing themselves with by the hour together. At all events, if it involved any secret information in regard to old Roger Chillingworth, it was in a tongue unknown to the **erudite** clergyman, and did but increase the bewilderment of his mind.

   Someone who is **erudite** is NOT

   a. uneducated   **c.** studious
   b. literate   **d.** cultured

5. "But now—since I am **irrevocably** doomed—wherefore should I not snatch the solace allowed to the condemned culprit before his execution?"

   The fate of one who is **irrevocably** doomed

   a. can be changed   **c.** is questionable
   b. is unfair   **d.** cannot be avoided

Interactive Quiz

Snap the code, or go to **vocabularyworkshop.com**

*Read the following selection, taking note of the **boldface** words and their contexts. These words are among those you will be studying in Unit 5. As you complete the exercises in this unit, it may help to refer to the way the words are used below.*

Lending a Hand to End Poverty

<Newspaper Article>

By WALTER Q. VOGEL   November 12

Washington, D.C.—A local charity that studies antipoverty programs has declared one particular activist's model a notable success. In its annual report, "Fighting Poverty Today," Global Poverty Watchers United (GPWU) hailed the work of Muhammad Yunus, whose pioneering microloan program has helped thousands of Bangladeshis rise out of poverty. The charity suggests that the concept of microcredit—lending people very small sums of money—be tried by governments around the world. "Poverty is a **scourge** that knows no borders," says the report's author, Anja Aziz-Ooka. "In every country in the world, we find people living a hardscrabble existence. For some of them, thanks to microloans, escaping poverty can be more than just a dream."

Yunus's work to alleviate poverty began in 1974 during a visit to his native Bangladesh. The American-educated economist was shocked by the widespread famine he witnessed in his home country. Yunus figured that if destitute people were able to obtain small loans, they might be able to **extricate** themselves from the clutches of poverty. His first set of loans, from his own pocket, went to 42 borrowers and amounted to just $27. Yunus trusted that the majority of recipients were honest and would not **filch** these very small sums but would instead repay the money once they got on their feet.

From tiny acorns mighty oaks grow. In 1983, Yunus founded the Grameen Bank to apply the principles of microcredit throughout Bangladesh. To date, Grameen Bank has given loans to more than eight million poor people in Bangladesh, 97 percent of whom are women. The bank has found that women are more likely than men to use the loans to create a more **equitable** society and better living

Muhammad Yunus at a speech in Germany.

conditions for their families. Borrowers use the loans to establish entrepreneurial ventures, such as a yogurt factory or village telephone service. The **salutary** effects of Grameen's microloans are undeniable: 58 percent of the bank's borrowers have now crossed over the poverty line and live better lives. The bank's loan repayment rate is a remarkable 97 percent.

In recognition of his efforts, Yunus was awarded the Nobel Peace Prize in 2006. As he accepted the Nobel Prize, Yunus made **scathing** comments about the living conditions that the poor must endure, and about the inequitable distribution of income worldwide. He pointed out that 60 percent of the global population lives on only 6 percent of the world's income. More than one billion people live on less than a dollar a day. His fame as a Nobel laureate and the success of the Grameen Bank have helped **blazon** the microfinance concept across the developing world. Yunus has issued a strong **caveat** to world leaders: Poverty, he believes, is a threat to peace.

This view is shared by scholars. "When human beings are trapped in a web of malnutrition, disease, and hopelessness, they lead a **sepulchral** existence," says Kevyn di Napoli, a researcher with the city Department of Social Assistance. "Poverty robs its victims of their **autonomy**, making them vulnerable to ruthless landlords and moneylenders and even the bullies of

This woman started a poultry farm with her Grameen loan.

organized crime." As a result, he notes, the desperately poor may become hostile and angry. "Inevitably, simply to survive, some will **flout** the law and social convention alike by turning to a life of crime."

One of Yunus's basic **precepts** is that poverty is the creation of poorly designed social and economic systems. Before the rise of microloan programs, it was **axiomatic** in banking circles that prospective borrowers had to have a job and collateral. Change in traditional banking practices has come at a **soporific** pace, says GPWU's Aziz-Ooka. "Too many bankers have been unimaginative, **straitlaced**, and unwilling to experiment with bold, new ideas." Clearly, microfinance is no **transient** phenomenon, as Yunus's forty years of success shows (he retired in 2011). Similar programs are being created across the developing world, from Malawi in Africa to Bolivia in South America. As Yunus asserted in his Nobel Prize acceptance speech, "We can create a poverty-free world if we collectively believe in it."

This woman started a dressmaking shop with her loan.

Snap the code, or go to **vocabularyworkshop.com**

Definitions

Note the spelling, pronunciation, part(s) of speech, and definition(s) of each of the following words. Then write the word in the blank spaces in the illustrative sentence(s) following. Finally, study the lists of synonyms and antonyms.

1. amnesty
(am' nə stē)

(*n.*) a general pardon for an offense against a government; in general, any act of forgiveness or absolution

Many political prisoners were freed under the
_____ granted by the new regime.

SYNONYM: reprieve

2. autonomy
(ô tän' ə mē)

(*n.*) self-government, political control

After the colonies gained _____ from England, many Americans still clung to English traditions.

SYNONYM: home rule; ANTONYMS: dependence, subjection

3. axiomatic
(ak sē ə mat' ik)

(*adj.*) self-evident, expressing a universally accepted principle

One should not accept the idea that the camera never lies as an _____ truth.

SYNONYM: taken for granted; ANTONYMS: questionable, dubious

4. blazon
(blāz' ən)

(*v.*) to adorn or embellish; to display conspicuously; to publish or proclaim widely

They will _____ the results of the election across the Internet and every television set in the land.

SYNONYMS: broadcast, trumpet; ANTONYMS: hide, conceal, bury

5. caveat
(kav' ē at)

(*n.*) a warning or caution to prevent misunderstanding or discourage behavior

The well-known Latin phrase " _____ emptor" means, "Let the buyer beware."

SYNONYMS: admonition, word to the wise

6. equitable
(ek' wə tə bəl)

(*adj.*) fair, just, embodying principles of justice

He did more work, so a sixty-forty split of the profits seemed an _____ arrangement.

SYNONYMS: right, reasonable, evenhanded
ANTONYMS: unjust, unfair, one-sided, disproportionate

7. extricate
(ek' strə kāt)

(*v.*) to free from entanglements or difficulties; to remove with effort

The ring must have slid off my finger as I was trying to
_____ the fish from the net.

SYNONYMS: disentangle, extract; ANTONYMS: enmesh, entangle

8. filch
(filch)

(*v.*) to steal, especially in a sneaky way and in petty amounts

If you _____ pennies from the cash drawer, you will be tempted to steal larger amounts one day.

SYNONYMS: pilfer, purloin, swipe

9. flout
(flaut)

(*v.*) to mock, treat with contempt

She chose to ignore my advice, not because she wanted to _____ my beliefs, but because she had strong opinions of her own.

SYNONYMS: sneer at, snicker at, scorn; ANTONYMS: obey, honor

10. fractious
(frak' shəs)

(*adj.*) tending to be troublesome; unruly, quarrelsome, contrary; unpredictable

It seems as if even the smoothest-running organizations contain one or two _____ elements.

SYNONYMS: refractory, recalcitrant, peevish
ANTONYMS: docile, tractable, cooperative

11. precept
(prē' sept)

(*n.*) a rule of conduct or action

Many philosophies follow the _____ that it is important to treat others as you would like to be treated.

SYNONYMS: principle, maxim

12. salutary
(sal' yə ter ē)

(*adj.*) beneficial, helpful; healthful, wholesome

The cute new puppy had a _____ effect on her health.

SYNONYMS: salubrious, curative
ANTONYMS: detrimental, deleterious

13. scathing
(skā' thiŋ)

(*adj.*) bitterly severe, withering; causing great harm

Sometimes a reasoned discussion does more to change people's minds than a _____ attack.

SYNONYMS: searing, harsh, savage; ANTONYMS: bland, mild

14. scourge
(skərj)

(*v.*) to whip, punish severely; (*n.*) a cause of affliction or suffering; a source of severe punishment or criticism

Jonathan Swift used wit to _____ the British government for its cruel treatment of Ireland.

Competing teams consider my daughter the _____ of the soccer field.

SYNONYMS: (*v.*) flog, beat; (*n.*) bane, plague, pestilence
ANTONYMS: (*n.*) godsend, boon, blessing

15. sepulchral
(sə pəl' krəl)

(adj.) funereal, typical of the tomb; extremely gloomy or dismal

In a severe and _____ tone of voice, my sister announced that we were out of cookies.

SYNONYMS: lugubrious, mortuary

16. soporific
(säp ə rif' ik)

(adj.) tending to cause sleep, relating to sleepiness or lethargy; (n.) something that induces sleep

He claimed that the musical was _____ and that he had slept through the entire second act.

Shakespeare's Juliet drinks a _____ so as to appear to be dead—a trick she is soon to regret.

SYNONYMS: (n.) narcotic, anesthetic
ANTONYMS: (adj.) stimulating; (n.) stimulant, stimulus

17. straitlaced
(strāt' lāst)

(adj.) extremely strict in regard to moral standards and conduct; prudish, puritanical

Travelers may find people overseas _____ in some ways but surprisingly free in others.

SYNONYMS: highly conventional, overly strict, stuffy
ANTONYMS: lax, loose, indulgent, permissive, dissolute

18. transient
(tran' shənt)

(adj.) lasting only a short time, fleeting; (n.) one who stays only a short time

His bad mood was _____, and by the time he'd finished his breakfast, he was smiling.

Many farm hands lived the lives of _____ during the Great Depression.

SYNONYMS: (adj.) impermanent, ephemeral, evanescent
ANTONYMS: (adj.) permanent, imperishable, immortal

19. unwieldy
(ən wēl' dē)

(adj.) not easily carried, handled, or managed because of size or complexity

We loaded the truck with the chairs and the coffee table, but the grand piano was too _____.

SYNONYMS: bulky, clumsy, impractical
ANTONYMS: manageable, easy to handle

20. vapid
(vap' id)

(adj.) dull, uninteresting, tiresome; lacking in sharpness, flavor, liveliness, or force

While critics called the movie _____, I thought the performers were very compelling.

SYNONYMS: lifeless, colorless; ANTONYMS: zesty, spicy, colorful

Choosing the Right Word

*Select the **boldface** word that better completes each sentence. You might refer to the selection on pages 60–61 to see how most of these words are used in context.*

1. I now know that *Gulliver's Travels*, far from being a "children's book," is a work of mature and (**scathlng, vapld**) satire.

2. The verbal sparring that took place between the two head coaches was (**blazoned, extricated**) across headlines nationwide.

3. You may regard her ideas as (**salutary, straitlaced**), but I think that they reflect good thinking and sound values.

4. The rules of the club proved so (**unwieldy, equitable**) that it was all but impossible to carry on business.

5. How easy it is for a nation to become trapped in an inflationary price rise; how difficult to (**blazon, extricate**) itself from the upward spiral!

Jonathan Swift, who wrote *Gulliver's Travels* and *A Modest Proposal,* was a master of satire.

6. I didn't expect the play to be particularly stimulating, but I certainly never anticipated its overwhelmingly (**equitable, soporific**) power.

7. Instead of brooding about past wrongs, I suggest that you declare a personal (**amnesty, caveat**) and start thinking about the future.

8. We had many talented players, but the (**fractious, scathing**) behavior of a few individuals impaired our team spirit and led to a losing season.

9. Arriving at (**fractious, equitable**) arrangements in human affairs often requires sound judgment, as well as good intentions.

10. Young people, tired of being controlled by parents, teachers, and others, often have a strong impulse to gain (**amnesty, autonomy**).

11. Appointed by the Governor to be Commissioner of Investigations, she soon became the (**scourge, autonomy**) of dishonest and incompetent officials.

12. Some sadly misguided individuals seem to go through life trying to (**filch, blazon**) petty advantages from everyone they encounter.

13. Try placing sachets of (**axiomatic, soporific**) herbs, such as lemon balm and lavender, inside your pillow if you suffer from insomnia.

14. The (**precept, scourge**) of plagiarism is on the rise in many schools as students cut and paste from essays they download from the Internet.

15. I intend to be guided by the simple (**scourges, precepts**) that have proven their value over long periods of human experience.

16. Unabridged dictionaries often alert the reader to common mistakes in the use of a word by including brief (**caveats, scourges**).

17. The newly elected judge ruled his courtroom with a king's (**amnesty, autonomy**), and no one dared to act in an unruly fashion.

18. Isn't it strange that the basic ideas that some economists regard as (**sepulchral, axiomatic**) are rejected by others as absolutely false!

19. Today our intricate network of mass communications can (**blazon, flout**) news of national importance across the country in a matter of minutes.

20. The ghost of Hamlet's father whispered in (**sepulchral, salutary**) tones the story of his tragic death.

21. Few things are more (**salutary, unwieldy**) for a young person than an occasional painful reminder that life is not a bowl of cherries.

22. In spite of the tremendous sales of that novel, I found it to be mediocre and (**salutary, vapid**) in every respect.

23. The popular self-help book teaches that material things are (**transient, fractious**), while moral values are eternal.

24. Young people who consider themselves nonconformists often go to extremes in their determination to (**blazon, flout**) the conventions.

25. Officials who took bribes were indicted with no hope of an (**amnesty, autonomy**).

Synonyms

*Choose the word from this unit that is the same or most nearly the same in meaning as the **boldface** word or expression in the phrase. Write that word on the line. Use a dictionary if necessary.*

1. guided by stern **rules** _____

2. a **doleful** atmosphere during the service _____

3. eager to **scoff at** the unknown _____

4. a **forewarning** regarding possible difficulties _____

5. too **cumbersome** to carry home _____

6. an **acquittal** for the former rebels _____

7. an **insipid** little five-note tune _____

8. **disengage** the cat from the tree _____

9. to **pocket** some coins from petty cash _____

10. an argumentative, **obstinate** congress _____

Antonyms

*Choose the word from this unit that is most nearly opposite in meaning to the **boldface** word or expression in the phrase. Write that word on the line. Use a dictionary if necessary.*

1. remaining **agreeable** under pressure _____
2. a water hose that is **controllable** _____
3. serving a **life sentence** in prison _____
4. medicine that acted as an **energizer** _____
5. attending a **lively** festival _____

Completing the Sentence

From the words in this unit, choose the one that best completes each of the following sentences. Write the word in the space provided.

1. I tried to warn them of the dangers involved in such an undertaking, but all my _____ and admonitions fell on deaf ears.

2. His fame as a football star proved to be _____, and he found himself just another young man looking for a job.

3. Even the most talented actors could not breathe life and credibility into the _____ lines of that silly play.

4. The carton was not heavy, but it was so _____ that it took four of us to carry it to the shed.

5. Failures are always unpleasant, but if you learn from them, they may have a(n) _____ effect on your future career.

6. The fighter planes of World War II sometimes had the pictures of famous movie stars, like Betty Grable, _____ on the fuselage.

7. My teacher's criticism of my term paper was so _____ that after reading it, I felt thoroughly crushed.

8. It became clear that the squad of police would be unable to control the small but _____ crowd of angry protesters.

9. Any unit of government—national or local—that _____ sound economic principles is headed for disaster.

10. The _____ effect of his droning lectures surpasses that of any sleeping pill now in use.

11. She has made so many contradictory promises to so many people that I don't see how she can _____ herself from the situation.

12. Her approach to the problem seems to have been guided by the time-honored _____ that "force is the remedy for nothing."

13. It is _____ that democracy, more than any other form of government, calls for the active participation of all the people in public affairs.

14. Since the close of World War II, almost one hundred former colonies have gained full _____ and joined the family of nations.

15. Shivers went up and down our spines as, in a(n) _____ voice, the teacher spoke to us of ghosts, vampires, and the "living dead."

16. The decision was a disappointment to me, but after thinking it over, I had to agree that it was _____.

17. Who would have thought that the new treasurer could sink so low as to _____ money from the club's petty cash fund?

18. The new government, seeking to restore normal conditions, declared a(n) _____ for all political prisoners.

19. The standards of behavior generally accepted in Victorian times would probably be rejected today as excessively _____.

20. It was Lincoln who said, "Fondly do we hope, fervently do we pray, that this mighty _____ of war may speedily pass away."

Writing: Words in Action

1. Look back at "Lending a Hand to End Poverty" (pages 60–61). Think about how poverty affects your own community. What solution would you propose to help alleviate poverty in your area? Write a letter to the editor of your local newspaper, describing the problem and offering a solution. Use at least two details from the passage and three unit words.

2. *"The greatest good you can do for another is not just to share your riches but to reveal to him his own."—attributed to Benjamin Disraeli*

Today, various individuals and organizations make small loans, or microloans, to people around the world, enabling them to better their lives by creating or maintaining their own businesses. How does the concept of the "microloan" relate to the quotation above? Do you agree that small loans can encourage people to become more self-sufficient, or do you think such loans can make people more dependent? In a brief essay, support your opinion using specific examples, observations, and the reading (pages 60–61). Write at least three paragraphs, and use three or more words from this unit.

Vocabulary in Context

Literary Text

The following excerpts are from **The Spy** *by James Fenimore Cooper. Some of the words you have studied in this unit appear in* **boldface** *type. Complete each statement below the excerpt by circling the letter of the correct answer.*

1. In person, the peddler was a man above the middle height, spare, but full of bone and muscle. At first sight, his strength seemed unequal to manage the **unwieldy** burden of his pack; yet he threw it on and off with great dexterity, and with as much apparent ease as if it had been filled with feathers.

    A backpack that is **unwieldy** is NOT

    a. burdensome   **c.** manageable
    b. heavy   **d.** awkward

2. It would have been a business of no small difficulty for any tribunal then existing in the new states to have enforced a restitution of the money; for it was shortly after most **equitably** distributed, by the hands of Sergeant Hollister, among a troop of horse.

    If money is **equitably** distributed, it is done so

    a. fairly   **c.** quickly
    b. quietly   **d.** slowly

3. ...Miss Peyton...had not thought it necessary to **blazon** the intended nuptials of her niece to the neighborhood, had even time been allowed; she thought, therefore, that she was now communicating a profound secret . . . .

    To **blazon** a wedding announcement is to

    a. praise it   **c.** conceal it
    b. denounce it   **d.** publicize it

James Fenimore Cooper wrote about colonial America.

4. He bent his body down, as if in pain, his fingers worked while the hands hung lifeless by his side, and there was an expression in his countenance that seemed to announce a writhing of the soul; but it was not unresisted, and it was **transient**.

    An expression that is **transient** is

    a. enduring   **c.** pleasant
    b. temporary   **d.** hollow

5. The English continued their retreat the moment they were **extricated** from their assailants; and Dunwoodie, who was severely, but not dangerously wounded, recalled his men from further attempts, which must be fruitless.

    Troops that are **extricated** from the enemy have

    a. prevailed   **c.** drawn back
    b. paused   **d.** moved forward

Interactive Quiz

Snap the code, or go to **vocabularyworkshop.com**

UNIT 6

*Read the following selection, taking note of the **boldface** words and their contexts. These words are among those you will be studying in Unit 6. As you complete the exercises in this unit, it may help to refer to the way the words are used below.*

Pre-Columbian America
<Blog Entry>

A teacher visiting pre-Columbian (before the time of Christopher Columbus) sites in Mexico during her summer break blogged about her experience for her students.

Near Mexico City, July 2011

Hello from Mexico! My hope is that everyone reading this blog lives my experiences **vicariously**. I'm sitting in a creaky, threadbare seat on a broiling, crowded bus. Far from feeling **ennui**, I am enjoying every minute of this sweaty bus ride because we are nearing the first great American city. Teotihuacán had 200,000 inhabitants a millennium before Columbus set foot in the Americas. It boasted broad avenues and stately pyramids as massive as the largest in Egypt. And to think that the first European arrivals cast **aspersions** on the native population groups they encountered, believing that they had landed on a continent peopled only by struggling farmers and hunter-gatherers.

Perhaps you recall learning in world history class that the European settlers, unaware of the widespread existence of formidable civilizations like this one, scorned the natives they met. These settlers directly or **surreptitiously** usurped lands that the local inhabitants had occupied for centuries, either **cajoling** them with trinkets, or else **contriving** other ways to cheat them. Had the Europeans only seen the fine pottery, masks, advanced calendars, glorious palaces and temples! But when the Europeans arrived in North America, they saw populations already decimated by diseases brought by earlier European fishermen and explorers. Pushing the weakened natives out was a **sinecure**.

Terracotta figure of Tlaloc, god of rain and water, from Teotihuacán

Pyramid of the Sun, Teotihuacán, Mexico

At Teotihuacán

It is not true that dead men tell no tales, because the long-gone population of Teotihuacán has left behind plenty that tells us of its great society. In front of me now is the spectacular Pyramid of the Sun. There is nothing **anomalous** about the engineering marvels at Teotihuacán. Great civilizations throughout the so-called new world lived in cities larger than those in Europe at the same time. **Fettered** by ignorance and ethnocentrism, people in Europe's capital cities would have found the idea of sophisticated cultures across the Atlantic completely **bizarre**; but had they seen the impressive Toltec, Mayan, Aztec, or Incan civilizations in their prime, they would have been **disabused** of the notion that the lands Columbus "discovered" always had been thinly populated and lightly tread upon.

I overheard a tour guide telling visitors that by the time the Europeans arrived, all the great civilizations that had built such astounding structures were crumbling or lost forever. Gone were the vast trading networks, the advanced metallurgy techniques, and the agricultural methods that **transmuted** barren land and steep hillsides into fertile growing land. Gone, too, were the all-powerful rulers who reigned as ruthlessly as did the most **heinous** kings in Europe, and who freely **castigated** their subjects for

transgressing even the pettiest of laws. What remained were tools, pottery shards, and remnants of fine roads and great temples.

End of a Great Day

After spending the day traveling back in time, I am now on the bus back to the modern world. I saw **immutable** proof that a great city in an advanced civilization once existed here, and I wonder how many of you know of Teotihuacán or have even heard of the huge but long-gone urban centers of Chaco and Cahokia in the United States. The true history of the Americas was misunderstood not only by the first European visitors, but by people in our own time. Thankfully, this is changing as new scholarship is transforming long-held beliefs about the nature of life in the Americas before Columbus. A "lightly tread-upon" continent? No way!

Snap the code, or go to
vocabularyworkshop.com

Definitions

Note the spelling, pronunciation, part(s) of speech, and definition(s) of each of the following words. Then write the word in the blank spaces in the illustrative sentence(s) following. Finally, study the lists of synonyms and antonyms.

1. anomalous
(ə nam' ə ləs)

(*adj.*) abnormal, irregular, departing from the usual

Feeling protective of my friend but knowing of his difficulties placed me in an _____ position.

SYNONYMS: exceptional, unusual, aberrant
ANTONYMS: normal, regular, customary, typical, ordinary

2. aspersion
(ə spər' zhən)

(*n.*) a damaging or derogatory statement; the act of slandering or defaming

Think twice before casting _____ on his honesty, for he might be telling the truth.

SYNONYMS: innuendo, calumny; ANTONYMS: endorsement, praise

3. bizarre
(bi zär')

(*adj.*) extremely strange, unusual, atypical

Years from now I will look at this picture and wonder what sort of _____ costume I was wearing.

SYNONYMS: grotesque, fantastic, outlandish
ANTONYMS: normal, typical, ordinary, expected

4. brusque
(brəsk)

(*adj.*) abrupt, blunt, with no formalities

His request for a large loan for an indefinite length of time was met with a _____ refusal.

SYNONYMS: tactless, ungracious; ANTONYMS: tactful, diplomatic

5. cajole
(kə jōl')

(*v.*) to coax, persuade through flattery or artifice; to deceive with soothing thoughts or false promises

With a smile, a joke, and a second helping of pie, she would _____ him into doing what she wanted.

SYNONYMS: wheedle, inveigle; ANTONYMS: coerce, force

6. castigate
(kas' tə gāt)

(*v.*) to punish severely; to criticize severely

After he _____ the unruly children, they settled down to study quietly.

SYNONYMS: chastise, censure; ANTONYMS: honor, praise, laud

7. contrive
(kən trīv')

(*v.*) to plan with ingenuity; to bring about through a plan

She can _____ wonderful excuses; but when she tries to offer them, her uneasiness gives her away.

SYNONYMS: think up, concoct, fabricate

8. demagogue
(dem′ ə gäg)

(*n.*) a leader who exploits popular prejudices and false claims and promises in order to gain power

Often a show of angry concern conceals the self-serving tactics of a _____.

SYNONYMS: rabble-rouser, firebrand

9. disabuse
(dis ə byüz′)

(*v.*) to free from deception or error, set right in ideas or thinking

He thinks that all women adore him, but my sister will probably _____ him of that idea.

SYNONYMS: undeceive, enlighten
ANTONYMS: deceive, delude, pull wool over one's eyes

10. ennui
(än wē′)

(*n.*) weariness and dissatisfaction from lack of occupation or interest, boredom

Some people seem to confuse sophistication with

_____.

SYNONYMS: languor, world-weariness, listlessness
ANTONYMS: enthusiasm, liveliness, excitement, intensity

11. fetter
(fet′ ər)

(*n.*) a chain or shackle placed on the feet (often used in plural); anything that confines or restrains; (*v.*) to chain or shackle; to render helpless or impotent

The old phrase "chain gang" refers to a group of prisoners forced to work, each one joined to the next by linked

_____.

It is said that good inventors do not _____ themselves with conventional thinking.

SYNONYMS: (*n.*) bond, restraint; (*v.*) bind, hamper
ANTONYMS: (*v.*) free, liberate, emancipate

12. heinous
(hā′ nəs)

(*adj.*) very wicked, offensive, hateful

A town so peaceful, quiet, and law-abiding was bound to be horrified by so _____ a crime.

SYNONYMS: evil, odious, outrageous
ANTONYMS: excellent, wonderful, splendid

13. immutable
(i myü′ tə bəl)

(*adj.*) not subject to change, constant

Scientists labored to discover a set of _____ laws of the universe.

SYNONYMS: unchangeable, unalterable, fixed, invariable
ANTONYMS: changeable, inconstant, variable, fickle

14. insurgent
(in sər′ jənt)

(*n.*) one who rebels or rises against authority; (*adj.*) rising in revolt, refusing to accept authority; surging or rushing in or on

George Washington and his contemporaries were _____ against Britain.

The army was confident that they could crush the _____ forces.

SYNONYMS: (*adj.*) revolutionary, rebellious, mutinous
ANTONYMS: (*adj.*) loyalist, loyal, faithful

15. megalomania
(meg ə lō mā′ nē ə)

(*n.*) a delusion marked by a feeling of power, wealth, talent, etc., far in excess of reality

Sudden fame and admiration can make people feel unworthy—or it can bring on feelings of _____.

SYNONYM: delusions of grandeur
ANTONYMS: modesty, self-abasement

16. sinecure
(si′ nə kyür)

(*n.*) a position requiring little or no work; an easy job

The office of Vice President of the United States was once considered little more than a _____.

SYNONYMS: "no-show" job, cushy job, "plum"

17. surreptitious
(sər əp tish′ əs)

(*adj.*) stealthy, secret, intended to escape observation; made or accomplished by fraud

The movie heroine blushed when she noticed the _____ glances of her admirer.

SYNONYMS: furtive, covert, clandestine, concealed
ANTONYMS: open, frank, aboveboard, overt

18. transgress
(tranz gres′)

(*v.*) to go beyond a limit or boundary; to sin, violate a law

The penitent citizens promised never again to _____ the laws of the land.

SYNONYMS: overstep, trespass; ANTONYMS: obey, toe the line

19. transmute
(tranz myüt′)

(*v.*) to change from one nature, substance, or form to another

To _____ distrust into cooperation along that war-torn border will take more than talk and treaties.

SYNONYMS: transform, convert; ANTONYMS: preserve, maintain

20. vicarious
(vī kâr′ ē əs)

(*adj.*) performed, suffered, or otherwise experienced by one person in place of another

In search of _____ excitement, we watched movies of action and adventure.

SYNONYMS: surrogate, secondhand; ANTONYMS: actual, firsthand

Choosing the Right Word

Select the **boldface** word that better completes each sentence. You might refer to the selection on pages 70–71 to see how most of these words are used in context.

1. Laura Ingalls Wilder's *Little House on the Prairie* books were so vivid that, as a child, I felt I was (**vicariously, surreptitiously**) experiencing the realities of pioneer life.

2. My uncle Rick seems unable to (**cajole, disabuse**) himself of the idea that he is still capable of the feats he performed in his youth.

3. Government bureaucracy was hobbling many programs with (**fetters, aspersions**) of red tape.

4. Many of Mark Twain's contemporaries found his essays amusing, but others cringed at his (**immutable, brusque**) commentary.

Laura Ingalls Wilder actually lived many of the experiences she described in her popular *Little House on the Prairie* books.

5. I cannot understand how she was able to (**disabuse, contrive**) a meeting between two people who had refused to have anything to do with each other.

6. A favorite ploy of the (**anomalous, demagogue**) is to appoint a convenient scapegoat upon whom a misguided populace can vent its anger.

7. The coach put his faith in his team, hoping they would not (**contrive, transgress**) the bounds of their training and violate protocol.

8. Her opinion of her own importance is so grotesquely exaggerated that we have come to regard her as a (**megalomaniac, demagogue**).

9. A(n) (**insurgent, heinous**) group at the convention refused to accept the choices of the regular party leaders.

10. His conduct after his mother's death was so (**anomalous, brusque**) that I must conclude he was not in full possession of his faculties.

11. With the innumerable activities open to a young person like you, I can't understand why you should suffer from (**ennui, megalomania**).

12. While Joan was sleeping soundly in her tent, oblivious to nocturnal creatures, a snake made its (**brusque, surreptitious**) way across the campsite.

13. Although her new position bore a high-sounding title, it was really little more than a(n) (**insurgent, sinecure**).

14. The task of education, said the speaker, is to (**transgress, transmute**) the primitive selfishness of the child into socially useful modes of behavior.

15. By casting (**sinecures, aspersions**) on the ability and character of others, you reveal the misgivings you have about yourself.

16. He's so tight with his money that it's just about impossible to (**cajole, transmute**) a nickel out of him, no matter how worthy the cause.

17. Living (**vicariously, immutably**) through her children, my neighbor pushes her sons and daughters into every extracurricular activity imaginable.

18. If, as they now claim, they were not aware of the illegal character of their undertaking, why did they plan it so (**cajolingly, surreptitiously**)?

19. Have you ever heard of anything as (**bizarre, brusque**) as an experimental technique to test the intelligence of cows?

20. For ancient Romans, fleeing from the battlefield was the most (**heinous, immutable**) act of cowardice a soldier could commit.

21. He may have kept within the letter of the law, but there is no doubt that he has (**cajoled, transgressed**) the accepted moral code.

22. The institutions of our society, far from being (**immutable, anomalous**), are in the process of change at this very moment.

23. In *Gulliver's Travels* and other writings, Jonathan Swift (**cajoled, castigated**) the human race for its follies and wickedness.

24. What hurt my feelings was not so much his refusal to give me a job as the (**brusque, vicarious**) way in which he told me that he had nothing for me.

25. I spent all morning trying to (**cajole, fetter**) our frightened cat out from under the house.

Synonyms

*Choose the word from this unit that is the same or most nearly the same in meaning as the **boldface** word or expression in the phrase. Write that word on the line. Use a dictionary if necessary.*

1. **abominable** treatment of prisoners of war   _____

2. an unwarranted **disparagement** against my friend   _____

3. trying to **limit** our imaginations   _____

4. the fear-mongering of an **agitator**   _____

5. **set straight** his mistaken belief   _____

6. wish to **rebuke** the vandals   _____

7. the disposition of a **radical**   _____

8. the cleverest plan we could **devise**   _____

9. behaves in such a **curt** manner   _____

10. the **self-regard** of power brokers   _____

Antonyms

*Choose the word from this unit that is most nearly opposite in meaning to the **boldface** word or expression in the phrase. Write that word on the line. Use a dictionary if necessary.*

1. his usual **gracious** reply _____

2. a conservative and **compliant** organization _____

3. the **humility** of the real genius _____

4. hearing the words of a **peace-promoting leader** _____

5. experienced **genuine** thrills at the race _____

Completing the Sentence

From the words in this unit, choose the one that best completes each of the following sentences. Write the word in the space provided.

1. Anyone who refers to my job as a(n) _____ should spend just one day in my place!

2. At the very outset of the term, I urged you to _____ yourself of the idea that you can pass this course without hard, regular work.

3. I welcome honest criticism, but I deeply resented their _____ on my sincerity and good faith.

4. Since he had always been quiet and retiring, we were amazed when he stood up at the meeting and _____ the chairperson for failing to give everyone a chance to speak.

5. The _____ way in which they planned the undertaking shows that they were aware of its illegal character.

6. The Emancipation Proclamation issued by Abraham Lincoln once and for all broke the _____ that bound African Americans to a life of servitude.

7. Is there any other crime in history as _____ as the attempt of the Nazis to annihilate so-called inferior racial groups?

8. In his determination to be blunt and honest, he has _____ the limits of good taste.

9. His conceit is so great and so immune to the lessons of experience that this must be considered a kind of _____.

10. Although the _____ were defeated by the government's forces, a small group escaped into the mountains, where it kept the spirit of rebellion alive.

11. I find it hard to understand how they were able to _____ such an elaborately underhanded scheme in so short a time.

12. Although most of us lead a quiet, humdrum sort of life, we can all get a(n) _____ thrill from the achievements of Olympic athletes.

13. The alchemists of the Middle Ages, who were both mystics and primitive chemists, hoped to _____ base metals into gold.

14. The one fact about nature that seems completely _____ is that everything is subject to change.

15. Wearing _____ masks at Halloween is a tradition that goes back many centuries.

16. His endless talk about himself and his interests produces _____ in others.

17. Resorting to rather farfetched promises, I finally _____ Tina into going to the prom with me.

18. Can you imagine anything as _____ as a successful drama coach who has never acted on the stage?

19. The speaker's blatant appeal to the emotions of the crowd smacked more of the _____ than of a true leader of the people.

20. Rude questions call for _____ answers, and mine is "No!"

Writing: Words in Action

1. Look back at "Pre-Columbian America" (pages 70–71). Pottery, calendars, palaces, and pyramids are some of the features that characterize the Toltec and Aztec civilizations of Mexico. Think about some of the features that exemplify modern-day civilization. Write a blog, comparing and contrasting a few aspects of modern life to life in pre-Columbian cultures. Use at least two details from the passage and three unit words.

2. Think about an ancient civilization you would like to learn more about firsthand. In a brief essay, describe a location you would like to visit, the ancient landmarks you would like to see there, and the kinds of experts you would like to consult in order to learn more about the aspects of that civilization that especially interest you. What can that civilization teach us? Support your essay with specific details, your studies, and the reading (pages 70–71). Write at least three paragraphs, and use three or more words from this unit.

Vocabulary in Context

Literary Text

The following excerpts are from The Works of Edgar Allan Poe, *Volume II. Some of the words you have studied in this unit appear in **boldface** type. Complete each statement below the excerpt by circling the letter of the correct answer.*

1. In many palaces, however, such suites form a long and straight vista, while the folding doors slide back nearly to the walls on either hand, so that the view of the whole extent is scarcely impeded. Here the case was very different; as might have been expected from the duke's love of the **bizarre**. The apartments were so irregularly disposed that the vision embraced but little more than one at a time. ("The Masque of the Red Death")

   Bizarre preferences are
   a. luxurious   c. trifling
   b. eccentric   d. conventional

2. I soon found him [Glendinning] of weak intellect, and, of course, marked him as a fitting subject for my skill. I frequently engaged him in play, and **contrived**, with the gambler's usual art, to let him win considerable sums, the more effectually to entangle him in my snares. ("William Wilson")

   Whenever something is **contrived**, it is
   a. judged   c. planned
   b. supervised   d. admired

3. A moment more and I had **fettered** him to the granite. In its surface were two iron staples, distant from each other about two feet, horizontally. ("The Cask of Amontillado")

   If someone is **fettered**, he or she is
   a. restrained   c. released
   b. fatigued   d. supported

4. I found D—at home, yawning, lounging, and dawdling, as usual, and pretending to be in the last extremity of **ennui**." ("The Purloined Letter")

   A person filled with **ennui** is NOT
   a. energetic   c. bored
   b. lethargic   d. fatigued

Vincent Price starred in several film adaptations of Poe's work, including *The Masque of the Red Death* (1964).

5. The patient, Mr. Edward Stapleton, had died, apparently of typhus fever, accompanied with some **anomalous** symptoms which had excited the curiosity of his medical attendants. ("The Premature Burial")

   Symptoms that are **anomalous** are
   a. deceptive   c. deliberate
   b. common   d. exceptional

Interactive Quiz

Snap the code, or go to **vocabularyworkshop.com**

Vocabulary for Comprehension

*Read the following selection in which some of the words you have studied in Units 4–6 appear in **boldface** type. Then answer the questions on page 81.*

This passage discusses the unlikely beginnings of one of today's most popular sports: basketball.

(Line)

Strange as it may seem, basketball was invented in the 1890s as an alternative to calisthenics and indoor marching at a YMCA school in
(5) Massachusetts. James Naismith, the physical education instructor at the school, noticed that his students, who played baseball in the spring and football in the fall, were not
(10) adequately challenged by indoor marching during New England's long, cold winters. Students' wintertime confinement, coupled with a lack of physical exertion, had
(15) a **soporific** effect. Naismith resolved to invent a new and **salutary** alternative.

To Naismith, it was **axiomatic** that the ideal team sport involved a ball
(20) and some sort of goal. But the new game, which would be played on a hard gym floor, had to be gentler than football. He chose a basket as a goal because the ball had to be
(25) dropped into it rather than hurled straight at it. To prevent **fractious** scuffles and to keep the defense from ganging up on the offense, Naismith placed the goals up
(30) beyond an average person's grasp.

In 1892 Naismith's first game was played by his entire eighteen-member gym class. But this proved too **unwieldy**, and the number of
(35) players on each side was later reduced and standardized to five. The sport proved lucky for Naismith. During the first women's basketball game, he met a teacher named
(40) Maude Sherman, whom he later married.

Colleges, including Vassar, Vanderbilt, and Yale, swiftly adopted the sport, and the YMCA formed
(45) several leagues of its own. Despite the benefits it offered, some **castigated** the game for being too rough; and a few YMCAs stuck to a schedule of good old-fashioned
(50) push-ups and marching instead. Basketball enthusiasts who still wanted to play the game simply rented dance halls or armories to compete in and charged admission
(55) in order to pay the rent. Professional basketball was born as a result of these admission fees; and in 1896, players in Trenton, New Jersey, were paid for the first time, $15 apiece, to
(60) compete in a game.

1. The meaning of **soporific** (line 15) is
   a. sleep-inducing
   b. debilitating
   c. exceptional
   d. frustrating
   e. stimulating

2. **Salutary** (line 16) is best defined as
   a. lucrative
   b. healthful
   c. exciting
   d. unsanitary
   e. deleterious

3. Which of the following best describes the main purpose of the first paragraph (lines 1–17)?
   a. to discuss why basketball was first played in New England
   b. to survey Naismith's career as a physical education instructor
   c. to explain why Naismith chose a basket as a goal
   d. to list reasons for the success of basketball as a sport
   e. to explain why Naismith invented basketball

4. **Axiomatic** (line 18) most nearly means
   a. self-evident
   b. meaningless
   c. redundant
   d. inconvenient
   e. ridiculous

5. Which of the following best describes the writer's organizational method in paragraph 2 (lines 18–30)?
   a. order of importance
   b. compare and contrast
   c. cause and effect
   d. order of impression
   e. chronological order

6. The meaning of **fractious** (line 26) is
   a. unnecessary
   b. confused
   c. frequent
   d. unruly
   e. hilarious

7. Which of the following inferences is supported by the passage?
   a. For some time after the sport's invention, only men played basketball.
   b. Basketball became more popular than football at many colleges.
   c. Women as well as men played basketball in the sport's early days.
   d. Basketball had no appeal to professional athletes.
   e. Many YMCAs refused to form basketball leagues.

8. **Unwieldy** (line 34) most nearly means
   a. confusing
   b. boring
   c. dangerous
   d. cumbersome
   e. rowdy

9. According to the passage, the standard number of players on each team is
   a. four
   b. five
   c. seven
   d. nine
   e. eighteen

10. **Castigated** (line 47) is best defined as
    a. rebuked
    b. attended
    c. praised
    d. disapproved of
    e. closed down

11. Which of the following best describes the author's tone in the passage?
    a. critical
    b. factual
    c. humorous
    d. indignant
    e. persuasive

12. Which would be the most appropriate form of publication for the passage?
    a. a Ph.D. dissertation in history
    b. a specialty sports magazine
    c. a widely circulated e-mail
    d. an encyclopedia entry
    e. a newspaper editorial

Two-Word Completions

Select the pair of words that best complete the meaning of each of the following passages.

1. "The American legal system is not _____, nor are our laws _____," the Chief Justice observed. "Like everything else in this fluid world of ours, they change and develop over time."
   a. anomalous . . . autonomous
   b. transient . . . resilient
   c. immutable . . . irrevocable
   d. axiomatic . . . inscrutable

2. When I returned from lunch earlier than I had planned, I surprised a little thief _____ attempting to _____ a few dollars from the petty cash drawer.
   a. brusquely . . . repudiate
   b. irrevocably . . . flout
   c. querulously . . . cajole
   d. surreptitiously . . . filch

3. Rubber's remarkable _____ to resume its original shape makes it one of the world's most _____ materials.
   a. aura . . . fractious
   b. propensity . . . resilient
   c. autonomy . . . erudite
   d. ennui . . . gossamer

4. "It took months of _____ effort and astute planning on my part to _____ this company from the mess in which I found it," the new owner smugly boasted. "If I hadn't worked like a dog, the firm would still be in financial hot water."
   a. amorphous . . . cajole
   b. sedulous . . . extricate
   c. immutable . . . contrive
   d. irrevocable . . . disabuse

5. Only the sound of my footsteps _____ through the empty hallway disturbed the _____ silence in which the deserted office building was enveloped. "It's as quiet as a tomb in here at night," I thought as I made my way to the exit.
   a. transgressing . . . gossamer
   b. exacting . . . anomalous
   c. reverberating . . . sepulchral
   d. transmuting . . . bizarre

6. He is usually so courteous and _____ that I was completely taken aback by his unaccountably _____ and surly reply to my question.
   a. affable . . . brusque
   b. fractious . . . scurrilous
   c. equitable . . . erudite
   d. straitlaced . . . querulous

7. She led such a(n) _____ life among her books and papers that her first outing in many years caused her to experience dismay at how _____ the neighborhood had become.
   a. insular . . . sleazy
   b. straitlaced . . . transmuted
   c. bizarre . . . heinous
   d. querulous . . . resilient

Proverbs

In the essay about Ada Byron, the talented mathematician and writer (see pages 50–51), the author claims that "the apple doesn't fall far from the tree." This saying is a proverb. What the author means is that Ada was very much like her famous father, poet Lord Byron. Ada inherited his gift for writing.

A **proverb** is a short saying that conveys a universal truth about life. Proverbs, which are based on common sense, offer words of wisdom and simple advice. Each culture has its own proverbs, passing them down from generation to generation. These metaphorical sayings become widespread and gradually enter our everyday language.

Choosing the Right Proverb

Read each sentence. Use context clues to figure out the meaning of each proverb in ***boldface*** *print. Then write the letter of the definition for the proverb in the sentence.*

1. I know you think I was cowardly not to confront her, but you have to admit that sometimes **discretion is the better part of valor**. _____

2. Since **good fences make good neighbors**, Jessica decided to plant a bamboo hedge between her property and her neighbor's back yard. _____

3. Though he tells people that he can fix anything, he is a **Jack of all trades and a master of none**. _____

4. There's no use trying to convince him now that he has made up his mind; **advice when most needed is least heeded**. _____

5. There was **no rest for the weary** after the ice storm, as we spent weeks removing fallen branches. _____

6. You really shouldn't spread gossip, since **a lie can travel around the world while the truth is still putting on her shoes**. _____

7. You have to let children make some mistakes so that they can learn from them. After all, **experience is the best teacher**. _____

8. **Don't bite off more than you can chew** if you really want to have more personal time. _____

9. I knew that Justin would be sad when his sister went off to college; **you never miss the water till the well has run dry**. _____

10. My grandparents believe that **variety is the spice of life**, so they travel frequently. _____

a. People won't listen to reason once they have made up their minds.

b. As soon as one task is done, another arises.

c. Sometimes it is better to be cautious than to run headlong into things.

d. We learn best by doing.

e. We miss the things we take for granted only when they are gone.

f. You should not take on more responsibilities than you can handle.

g. Life is more interesting when you experience a variety of things.

h. Someone who dabbles in many things but does not excel in any

i. Rumors and lies always get around faster than the truth.

j. Boundaries between people help maintain good relations.

Writing with Proverbs

Find the meaning of each proverb. (Use an online or print dictionary if necessary.) Then write a sentence for each proverb.

1. Hindsight is always twenty-twenty.

_____

2. Absence makes the heart grow fonder.

_____

3. Honesty is the best policy.

_____

4. A penny saved is a penny earned.

_____

5. A picture is worth a thousand words.

_____

_____

6. Look before you leap.

_____

_____

7. Loose lips sink ships.

_____

_____

8. Rome wasn't built in a day.

_____

9. Love is blind.

_____

10. All's well that ends well.

_____

11. Failing to plan is planning to fail.

_____

12. All that glitters is not gold.

_____

Denotation and Connotation

A dictionary definition provides the **denotation** of a word. The denotation is the word's objective, formal meaning. The **connotation** of a word is its implied or informal meaning, which includes positive or negative emotional associations.

Suppose you were writing an article about the cat family. To describe lions, you might use words such as *ferocious* or *majestic*. If you were writing about a pet cat, you would more likely choose words such as *frisky* or *cuddly*.

Consider these synonyms for the neutral word *sedulous*:

industrious   *persistent*   *insistent*   *pushy*

Industrious and *persistent* have positive connotations, whereas *insistent* and *pushy* have negative connotations.

> **Think:** A successful entrepreneur is *industrious* and *persistent*, but a scam artist is *insistent* and *pushy*.

Look at these examples of words. Notice how the connotation of each word varies.

NEUTRAL	POSITIVE	NEGATIVE
flexible	resilient	spongy
warning	caveat	alarm
increase	amplify	aggrandize

A word's connotation affects word choice, especially in persuasive writing or advertising. A subtle shade of meaning can make a huge impact on a prospective customer. Which would you rather purchase, the "thrifty tour" or the "priceless getaway cruise"?

Shades of Meaning

Write a plus sign (+) in the box if the word has a positive connotation.
Write a minus sign (–) if the word has a negative connotation. Put a zero (0)
if the word is neutral.

1. archetype ☐   **2.** querulous ☐   **3.** affable ☐   **4.** repudiate ☐

5. filch ☐   **6.** propensity ☐   **7.** axiomatic ☐   **8.** contraband ☐

9. salutary ☐   **10.** autonomy ☐   **11.** fetter ☐   **12.** amnesty ☐

13. scathing ☐   **14.** amorphous ☐   **15.** insular ☐   **16.** erudite ☐

Expressing the Connotation

Read each sentence. Select the word in parentheses that expresses the connotation (positive, negative, or neutral) given at the beginning of the sentence.

negative   **1.** It never ceases to amaze me that (**sleazy, disreputable**) politicians often avoid getting caught.

positive   **2.** My (**refined, straitlaced**) mother does not approve of the language that comedians use on late-night television.

neutral   **3.** Our old ice chest was too (**large, unwieldy**) to carry down to the beach, so we decided to purchase one that has wheels.

positive   **4.** My parents do not approve when I fail to live up to certain expectations, but at least their reprimands are (**impersonal, equitable**).

negative   **5.** Details about the (**heinous, grave**) crime were censored as the detectives searched for a suspect.

neutral   **6.** People who are (**firm, immutable**) in their beliefs tend to resist progress, even when the entire community would benefit.

positive   **7.** I just read a biography about Salvador Dalí and his (**bizarre, fantastic**) art.

negative   **8.** David is usually polite, so when he spoke to the reporters in such a (**brusque, firm**) manner, people assumed something was wrong.

Challenge: Using Connotation

Choose vocabulary words from Units 4–6 to replace the highlighted words in the sentences below. Then explain how the connotation of the replacement word changes the tone of the sentence.

disabused	transgressed	contrived
scourging	blazoned	flouting

1. Punishing _____ officers for petty offenses was a practice that changed when the new police chief took control of the force.

_____

_____

2. Upon waking, we were shocked to read the headlines **displayed** _____ on the front page of the newspaper.

_____

_____

3. When the main character **conspired** _____ to set up a complicated sting operation involving his twin brother, the film became exciting.

_____

_____

Classical Roots

grad, gress—to step, walk

The root *gress* appears in **transgress** (page 74). The literal meaning is "to step beyond." The word now means "to go beyond a limit or bound" or "to violate a command or law." Some other words based on the same root are listed below.

aggressive	digress	gradient	regress
congress	egress	gradualism	retrograde

From the list of words above, choose the one that corresponds to each of the brief definitions below. Write the word in the blank space in the illustrative sentence below the definition. Use a dictionary if necessary.

1. a meeting (*especially of persons or minds*)

We were invited to attend a(n) _____ of medical workers.

2. a policy of approaching a desired end by slight degrees

The moderates advocate a policy of _____.

3. a part (*as of a road or path*) that slopes upward or downward

The climbers struggled up the dangerously steep _____.

4. moving backward, contrary to the usual or normal order; tending toward a worse state

They resisted the _____ tendencies of the small but vocal faction.

5. to turn aside, get off the main topic (*"to step away"*)

She tried not to _____ from her speech.

6. to move backward; to decline, grow worse

Their reading skills will _____ if they do not study over the summer.

7. attacking, taking the first step in an attack or quarrel; energetic, forceful (*"walking toward"*)

Most wild animals are not _____ toward humans.

8. an exit; a going out (*"walking out"*)

We could not find a means of _____.

*Read the following selection, taking note of the **boldface** words and their contexts. These words are among those you will be studying in Unit 7. As you complete the exercises in this unit, it may help to refer to the way the words are used below.*

An Overlooked Exploration
<Informational Essay>

The USS *Vincennes* in Antarctica, 1840

On May 18, 1836, the U.S. Congress authorized an expedition to explore the Pacific Ocean and the South Seas. Its aim was to extend "the bounds of science and to promote knowledge." The four-year voyage achieved both goals, covering 87,000 miles between 1838 and 1842. However, this important journey remains relatively unknown today compared with Lewis and Clark's comparatively modest two-year, 8,000-mile expedition to the Pacific Coast.

Congress did not need to **concoct** a **grandiose** justification for authorizing $300,000 for the Ex. Ex., as the U.S. South Seas Exploring Expedition was called. The promise of information about newly discovered lands and unfamiliar peoples captivated curious readers across the nation. To military leaders, such information would be both useful and strategic. A third, and not **inconsequential**, factor was economic: New lands meant new opportunities for American businesses. Notable support came from New England's

wealthy whalers, whose industry—one of the most important and powerful at that time—faced growing demand for whale products and now sought new hunting territory. To **mitigate** the decline of their quarry, whalers had begun sending ships into the unfamiliar Antarctic waters. These **vulnerable** vessels often foundered on unknown hazards, causing shipwrecks. Such disasters meant both a loss of life and (**crass** as it may seem to point out) a loss of profits as well. Thus, there was great support in the United States for a voyage that would tell Americans more about far-away lands and waters.

The six ships of the Ex. Ex. sailed from Virginia on August 18, 1838, under the command of Charles Wilkes (1798–1877), the head of the Navy's strategic information-gathering Department of Charts and Instruments. The flotilla headed down to South America, rounded Cape Horn, and made a side trip to the Antarctic. From there, it sailed up the west coast of South America, then over to Tahiti, the Fiji

Islands, and Australia. The squad went on to the Hawaiian Islands, continuing east to the Pacific Northwest, then sailed home to New York via Manila, Singapore, and Cape Town. It was a circuitous route that might **disconcert** all but the most skillful navigators. However, the route proved productive: The **stalwart** seafarers produced 241 navigational charts, mapped 1,500 desolate, rocky miles of **austere** Antarctic coast (a landmass they named), and explored some 200 Pacific islands. In addition, the team charted the Northwest coastline, boosting American claims to the Oregon Territory, the Columbia River, Puget Sound, and the San Francisco Bay.

The officers and the civilian experts were **punctilious** about their scientific duties. As the Navy required, the crew filled journals with observations and maps, and it gathered thousands of natural specimens and ethnographic objects—plants and animals, corals and fossils, baskets and weapons—that the vast trove led to the founding, in 1846, of the Smithsonian Institution in Washington, D.C. Despite these many treasures, misery marked the mission. Wilkes was a **redoubtable** leader with great scientific talent, yet he was arrogant and later proved cruel as well. Before setting sail, Wilkes attempted to dismiss civilian experts in the belief that nonmilitary men would **debase** the Navy's noble endeavor. At sea, he pushed both himself and crew members hard, often **reproving** those he thought laggards.

Captain Charles Wilkes

He showed little mercy. In 1840, Pacific Islanders slaughtered two **cadaverous** sailors who had gone ashore in search of food to augment their scant rations. Wilkes offered the killers no opportunity to make **restitution**. Instead, the expedition attacked, leading to the deaths of 80 people. In Wilkes's defense, his men did not, in further retribution, **desecrate** holy places or **pillage** villages. On the whole, however, his **beneficent** acts were few. Although Wilkes named geographical features after crew members, this gesture failed to offset the brutal floggings he ordered for minor **infractions** of Naval regulations.

When the expedition arrived in New York City on June 10, 1842, Wilkes got his just deserts. Brought to court, he faced a court-martial but was acquitted of all charges except that of ordering illegally harsh punishments. It was a tumultuous trial and a sad ending to a spectacular expedition. With the advent of the Civil War, the triumphs of the Ex. Ex. soon drifted from contemporary consciousness. Yet the horrors of the expedition live on in fiction. Herman Melville used accounts of Wilkes's dictatorial conduct when he created the character of Ahab, the tyrannical captain in his 1851 novel *Moby-Dick*.

The Smithsonian Institution, circa 1847–1865

iWords

Snap the code, or go to **vocabularyworkshop.com**

Definitions

Note the spelling, pronunciation, part(s) of speech, and definition(s) of each of the following words. Then write the word in the blank spaces in the illustrative sentence(s) following. Finally, study the lists of synonyms and antonyms.

1. austere
(ô stēr')

(*adj.*) severe or stern in manner; without adornment or luxury, simple, plain; harsh or sour in flavor

The _____ clothing and conduct of the Puritans expressed their humility.

SYNONYMS: forbidding, rigorous, puritanical, ascetic, unadorned
ANTONYMS: mild, indulgent, luxurious, flamboyant

2. beneficent
(bə nef' ə sənt)

(*adj.*) performing acts of kindness or charity; conferring benefits, doing good

From them I learned that purely _____ acts can require as much hard work as a nine-to-five job.

SYNONYMS: humanitarian, magnanimous, charitable
ANTONYMS: selfish, cruel, harmful, deleterious

3. cadaverous
(kə dav' ər əs)

(*adj.*) pale, gaunt, resembling a corpse

The rescued captives were weak from hunger and _____ in appearance.

SYNONYMS: corpselike, wasted, haggard, emaciated, ghastly
ANTONYMS: robust, portly, rosy, the picture of health

4. concoct
(kän käkt')

(*v.*) to prepare by combining ingredients, make up (as a dish); to devise, invent, fabricate

He _____ a savory stew with fresh herbs and vegetables from the garden.

SYNONYMS: create, fashion, rustle up

5. crass
(kras)

(*adj.*) coarse, unfeeling; stupid

We feel that the positions of our representative show a _____ indifference to our problems.

SYNONYMS: crude, tasteless, oafish, obtuse
ANTONYMS: refined, elegant, tasteful, polished, brilliant

6. debase
(di bās')

(*v.*) to lower in character, quality, or value; to degrade, adulterate; to cause to deteriorate

Every time a new rule is introduced in a popular sport, there are fans who say it will _____ the game.

SYNONYMS: cheapen, corrupt, demean, depreciate
ANTONYMS: elevate, uplift, improve, enhance

7. desecrate
(des′ ə krāt)

(v.) to commit sacrilege upon, treat irreverently; to contaminate, pollute

The search continues for the vandals who _____ the cemetery.

SYNONYMS: profane, defile, violate
ANTONYMS: revere, venerate, consecrate

8. disconcert
(dis kən sərt′)

(v.) to confuse; to disturb the composure of

They had hoped to _____ him with an unexpected question, but he was well prepared.

SYNONYMS: upset, rattle, ruffle, faze
ANTONYMS: relax, calm, put at ease

9. grandiose
(gran′ dē ōs)

(adj.) grand in an impressive or stately way; marked by pompous affectation or grandeur, absurdly exaggerated

In how many stories, I wonder, does an ambitious villain become the victim of _____ plans?

SYNONYMS: majestic, bombastic, highfalutin
ANTONYMS: simple, modest, humble

10. inconsequential
(in kän sə kwen′ shəl)

(adj.) trifling, unimportant

Feel free to ignore the _____ details, provided that you know exactly which ones they are.

SYNONYMS: trivial, negligible, paltry
ANTONYMS: important, essential, crucial

11. infraction
(in frak′ shən)

(n.) a breaking of a law or obligation

His uncle paid a fine for his _____ of the local recycling regulations.

SYNONYMS: violation, transgression, offense

12. mitigate
(mit′ ə gāt)

(v.) to make milder or softer, to moderate in force or intensity

I had hoped to _____ her anger by offering an apology.

SYNONYMS: lessen, relieve, alleviate
ANTONYMS: aggravate, intensify, irritate, exacerbate

13. pillage
(pil′ ij)

(v.) to rob of goods by open force (as in war), plunder; (n.) the act of looting; booty

The commanding officer warned his troops not to _____ the conquered city.

In Europe during the Dark Ages, _____ and murder became facts of life.

SYNONYMS: (v.) ravage, sack, loot; (n.) booty

14. prate
(prāt)

(*v.*) to talk a great deal in a foolish or aimless fashion
  He would _____ endlessly about the past but say nothing useful about our present dilemma.
  SYNONYMS: prattle, blab, palaver; ANTONYM: come to the point

15. punctilious
(pəŋk til' ē əs)

(*adj.*) very careful and exact, attentive to fine points of etiquette
  The clerk was so _____ in obeying court rules that I had to remind him why I was there.
  SYNONYMS: precise, scrupulous; ANTONYMS: careless, perfunctory

16. redoubtable
(ri daŭ' tə bəl)

(*adj.*) inspiring fear or awe; illustrious, eminent
  As a ruler he was _____, but, like all such rulers, he was not much loved.
  SYNONYMS: formidable, august; ANTONYMS: laughable, risible

17. reprove
(ri prüv')

(*v.*) to find fault with, scold, rebuke
  She _____ her staff for having followed orders blindly.
  SYNONYMS: chastise, upbraid, reproach
  ANTONYMS: praise, commend, laud, pat on the back

18. restitution
(res tə tü' shən)

(*n.*) the act of restoring someone or something to the rightful owner or to a former state or position; making good on a loss or damage
  They made _____ for the damage to the car but never fully regained the friendship of its owner.
  SYNONYMS: reimbursement, redress, restoration

19. stalwart
(stôl' wərt)

(*adj.*) strong and sturdy; brave; resolute; (*n.*) a brave, strong person; a strong supporter; one who takes an uncompromising position
  She became as _____ on the basketball court as she was quick at mathematical puzzles.
  The enemy had broken through our first line but was repulsed by the _____ defending the gates.
  SYNONYMS: (*adj.*) sturdy, stout, intrepid, valiant; (*n.*) mainstay
  ANTONYMS: (*adj.*) weak, infirm, irresolute, vacillating

20. vulnerable
(vəl' nər ə bəl)

(*adj.*) open to attack; capable of being wounded or damaged; unprotected
  Those brave enough to have opposed the dictator's rise now found themselves in a _____ position.
  SYNONYMS: defenseless, unguarded
  ANTONYMS: invincible, protected, safe, secure

Choosing the Right Word

*Select the **boldface** word that better completes each sentence. You might refer to the essay on pages 88–89 to see how most of these words are used in context.*

1. All the power of Great Britain could not shake the American colonists in their (**stalwart, beneficent**) opposition to measures that they considered unfair and tyrannical.

2. The fact that he did everything possible to help the poor child after the accident tends to (**mitigate, desecrate**) his responsibility for the tragedy.

3. Andrew (**desecrated, prated**) incessantly for an hour but made few insightful points.

4. The starving drought victims looked more like (**cadavers, stalwarts**) than living people.

5. The woman is known and loved throughout the community for her many (**redoubtable, beneficent**) acts on behalf of all types of unfortunates.

Thomas Paine challenged Britain's monarchy in his pamphlet *Common Sense.*

6. Some people find Francisco Goya's later works, known as the Black Paintings, (**disconcerting, punctilious**) because of their horrific, gloomy nature.

7. That sum may seem (**vulnerable, inconsequential**) to you, but to me it is a great deal of money.

8. His (**grandiose, beneficent**) schemes for world conquest collapsed in a nightmare of military defeat and internal revolt.

9. As (**restitution, infraction**) for the damage he had caused to the family car, Phil promised to clean and polish it regularly for a full year.

10. Her self-confidence is so unshakeable that she is simply not (**grandiose, vulnerable**) to "put-down" remarks that would annoy other people.

11. By concentrating on personal gain, he has (**debased, disconcerted**) both himself and the high office to which he was elected.

12. I have met few people who enjoy living an (**inconsequential, austere**) life of plain food, few possessions, and little sleep.

13. The principal (**disconcerted, reproved**) the entire student body for its discourteous behavior toward the guest speaker at the school assembly.

14. The sale of so many great works of art to foreign collectors is, in my eyes, little more than (**pillage, mitigation**) of our cultural heritage.

15. Although his conduct may not have violated any law, I consider it a gross (**cadaver, infraction**) of conventional ethical standards.

16. She is such a (**redoubtable, crass**) foe of the trite phrase that her students tremble lest her wrath descend on them for using a cliché.

17. In her clumsy efforts to be recognized as an "intellectual," she (**desecrates, prates**) endlessly about matters she does not really understand.

18. When we were children, my brother always got to play the role of the showy superhero, while I would take the part of the (**crass, stalwart**) and faithful sidekick.

19. It is a (**desecration, restitution**) of the memory of Lincoln to involve his name in defense of such a racist policy.

20. Since my next paycheck was not to be had until the first of the month, I reconciled myself to living (**austerely, inconsequentially**) until then.

21. The master chef has (**debased, concocted**) a dessert so rich that it will be a menace to weight watchers throughout the country.

22. He is so (**punctilious, austere**) about every detail that it is said he irons his shoelaces before wearing them.

23. The conductor of the orchestra was so (**desecrated, disconcerted**) by the noisy audience that he stopped the performance and asked for quiet.

24. Whenever I go to a concert, I seem to spend half my time shushing the (**crass, austere**) boors who chitchat while the orchestra is playing.

25. Tommy had (**grandiose, beneficent**) plans to build a stately mansion.

Synonyms

*Choose the word from this unit that is the same or most nearly the same in meaning as the **boldface** word or expression in the phrase. Write that word on the line. Use a dictionary if necessary.*

1. not **perturbed** by the noise _____

2. **vulgar** appeal for money _____

3. to **chatter** tediously about the weather _____

4. **compensation** for his misdeeds _____

5. **diminish** the horror of the crime _____

6. **cooked up** a silly excuse _____

7. exaggerating **minor** flaws _____

8. a **breach** of our agreement _____

9. **exposed** to wind and high water _____

10. **raid** the museum of valuables _____

Antonyms

*Choose the word from this unit that is most nearly opposite in meaning to the **boldface** word or expression in the phrase. Write that word on the line. Use a dictionary if necessary.*

1. **spoke concisely** about the new law   _____

2. her **unaffected** delivery of Shakespeare's lines   _____

3. **honor** this tribal ritual   _____

4. **contemptible** as a challenger   _____

5. **negligent** in filling out the form   _____

Completing the Sentence

From the words in this unit, choose the one that best completes each of the following sentences. Write the word in the space provided.

1. At a time when we need a modest, low-cost housing program, how can we be expected to accept such a(n) _____ scheme?

2. Who can ever forget those pictures showing the _____ faces of the people who had been in concentration camps!

3. Fond remembrances of happy days of family life intensified rather than _____ her grief.

4. She has _____ her considerable talents by writing books that are designed to appeal to the lowest tastes.

5. Our democracy, I believe, is more _____ to decay from within than it is to attack from the outside.

6. Though most of our players were the equals of theirs, the large size of their _____ team intimidated us.

7. I became desperately tired of listening to him _____ about how important he was, how much money he had, and so forth.

8. We are, I trust, long past the time when it was considered quite "natural" for newly elected officials to _____ the city treasury.

9. Before they arrived home from the party, they _____ an elaborate story that they hoped would excuse their being two hours late.

10. An official who is responsible for shaping vital national policies should not waste time and energy on such _____ matters.

11. I'm telling you this not to _____ you for having made a mistake but to prevent the mistake from being repeated.

12. They _____ the funeral service by talking loudly during the ceremonies, laughing, and generally showing a complete lack of respect.

13. He went right on with his speech, refusing to be _____ by the heckling of a few loudmouths.

14. I found that beneath his rather _____ manner and appearance there was a warm, sympathetic person.

15. His work on behalf of the homeless was merely the latest in a long line of _____ undertakings.

16. Though she looked rather frail, her _____ spirit made her a tireless crusader for women's rights.

17. Even a so-called minor _____ of the traffic laws may lead to a serious accident.

18. Is there any way that we can make _____ for the terrible wrong we have done them?

19. Whenever she serves as chairperson, she is so _____ that she insists on observing every fine point of parliamentary procedure.

20. It is hard to forgive the _____ selfishness with which they took most of the food supplies for their own use.

Writing: Words in Action

1. Look back at "An Overlooked Exploration" (pages 88–89). Suppose that you are a news reporter in 1842, the year Wilkes returned from his expedition. Write an editorial in which you explain and support your opinion about Wilkes's expedition and his role as a leader. Use at least two details from the passage and three unit words.

2. *"Do not go where the path may lead; go instead where there is no path and leave a trail."*—Ralph Waldo Emerson

   Do you agree with Emerson's statement? Think of some literal and figurative "paths" and "trails" in life. What are the risks and rewards of creating a trail where there was not one before? Is making a new trail something anyone can do, or do only exceptional people make new trails? Write your ideas in a brief essay. Support your points with specific details, personal experience, your studies, and the reading (pages 88–89). Write at least three paragraphs, and use three or more words from this unit.

Vocabulary in Context

Literary Text

The following excerpts are from **Main Street** by Sinclair Lewis. Some of the words you have studied in this unit appear in **boldface** type. Complete each statement below the excerpt by circling the letter of the correct answer.

1. Carol drove through an astonishing number of books from the public library and from city shops. Kennicott was at first uncomfortable over her **disconcerting** habit of buying them. A book was a book, and if you had several thousand of them right here in the library, free, why the dickens should you spend your good money?

   Something that is **disconcerting** is
   - **a.** alarming
   - **b.** enlightening
   - **c.** effortless
   - **d.** expensive

2. Carol's family were self-sufficient in their inventive life, with Christmas a rite full of surprises and tenderness, and "dressing-up parties" spontaneous and joyously absurd. The beasts in the Milford hearth-mythology were not the obscene Night Animals who jump out of closets and eat little girls, but **beneficent** and bright-eyed creatures....

   A creature that is **beneficent** is NOT
   - **a.** obliging
   - **b.** sympathetic
   - **c.** generous
   - **d.** greedy

3. "We haven't seen you at the library yet," Miss Villets **reproved**.

   "I've wanted to run in so much but I've been getting settled and—I'll probably come in so often you'll get tired of me! I hear you have such a nice library."

   If you are **reproved** you are
   - **a.** noticed
   - **b.** chided
   - **c.** challenged
   - **d.** assessed

In 1930, Sinclair Lewis became the first American to win a Nobel Prize for literature.

4. ...[T]o Hugh, Olaf was lord among mortal men, less **stalwart** than the old monarch, King Miles, but more understanding of the relations and values of things, of small sticks, lone playing-cards, and irretrievably injured hoops.

   A person who is **stalwart** is
   - **a.** jovial
   - **b.** reserved
   - **c.** steadfast
   - **d.** delicate

5. "Think how much better you can criticize conventional customs if you yourself live up to them, scrupulously. Then people can't say you're attacking them to excuse your own **infractions**."

   Infractions involve behavior considered to be
   - **a.** offensive
   - **b.** intimidating
   - **c.** appropriate
   - **d.** fashionable

Snap the code, or go to **vocabularyworkshop.com**

*Read the following selection, taking note of the **boldface** words and their contexts. These words are among those you will be studying in Unit 8. As you complete the exercises in this unit, it may help to refer to the way the words are used below.*

Mythical Journeys

<Humorous Essay>

In the long centuries before innovations in the technology of sailing ships enabled Western Europeans to conquer oceans and explore the world, the medieval European imagination was a rowdy and **intemperate** creature. Most Europeans spent their lives tied to the lands they were born in, so news from distant places was hard to come by, and even harder to trust. Lacking reliable knowledge of the world, people were **susceptible** to all manner of fantastic belief. Calm, **dispassionate** thinking was **relegated** to the background while imagination ran full throttle. Careful judgment was **subservient** to superstition and shaky **hypothetical** claims. Fables about foreign lands were frequently accepted as facts.

A notorious example of fiction erroneously taken for fact in those superstitious times is *The Travels of Sir John Mandeville.* Written in the 14th century, the book recounts the journeys of an English knight who leaves England and travels through the East. Along the way, so the story goes, Sir John stumbles across an island of *cynocephalus*— creatures with bodies of humans and heads of dogs. Elsewhere, he finds one tribe that relies for nourishment on the very smell of apples, and another tribe of tiny folks with mouths so small they have to slurp their meals through reeds. In another strange land, he discovers fish leaping out of the sea to offer themselves up as food; monstrous, **corpulent** worms with heads the size of a man's thigh; and humongous snails so massive that the locals use their shells for homes.

In our enlightened times, practically anyone you meet would **disavow** belief in such fanciful claims, but for over a century after the book was written, many took it for a trusty source of information about the world beyond Europe's horizons. Perhaps the lack of **dissension** in this matter owed something to the fact that, along with all

the tales of fabulous creatures and peoples, the book is full of accurate geographical accounts, which, incredibly, would have made it useful to travelers of the day. Indeed, with so many medieval sources blending fact and fiction, it would take centuries before explorers and geographers learned to **expurgate** the fables from the record of history.

Consider the plight of Christopher Columbus, the most celebrated voyager ever to have taken up the **gauntlet** and accepted the challenge of exploration. In a letter to his Spanish patrons, we find a befuddled Columbus reporting that, to his **consternation**, he hasn't encountered a single monster during his voyage. He even apologizes, afraid this shortcoming might **impugn** his reputation. As far as old Columbus was concerned, part of his job was to track down the dog-headed men, one-eyed giants, and other fabulous creatures the travelers of his day took for granted—thanks, in part, to the wondrous tales of Sir John Mandeville. But try as he might... well, the fact is Columbus never found them.

Superstitious belief in the tall tales of legendary travelers began to **dissipate** in the 17th and 18th centuries. In the end,

the air of **odium** that eventually came to surround such beliefs probably resulted from increased familiarity with our planet Earth, as much as it might have been caused by any change in the intellectual climate. As exploration gradually covered the entire globe, it just turned out that there weren't any dog-headed men after all, and nothing cuts down superstition like a long, hard look at the facts.

iWords™

Snap the code, or go to **vocabularyworkshop.com**

Definitions

Note the spelling, pronunciation, part(s) of speech, and definition(s) of each of the following words. Then write the word in the blank spaces in the illustrative sentence(s) following. Finally, study the lists of synonyms and antonyms.

1. acrimonious
(ak rə mō′ nē əs)

(*adj.*) stinging, bitter in temper or tone

She whirled to face me when I spoke, and her answer startled me by its _____ intensity.

SYNONYMS: biting, rancorous, hostile, peevish
ANTONYMS: gentle, warm, mild, cordial

2. bovine
(bō′ vīn)

(*adj.*) resembling a cow or ox; sluggish, unresponsive

After I told him what had happened, he sat there with a _____ expression and said nothing.

SYNONYMS: stolid, dull, slow, stupid
ANTONYMS: sharp, bright, keen, quick

3. consternation
(kän stər nā′ shən)

(*n.*) dismay, confusion

His father looked at the mess with _____, hardly knowing what to say first.

SYNONYMS: shock, amazement, bewilderment, dismay
ANTONYMS: calm, composure, aplomb

4. corpulent
(kôr′ pyə lənt)

(*adj.*) fat; having a large, bulky body

Though she had grown _____ with the years, the opera singer's voice and her way with a song were the same.

SYNONYMS: overweight, heavy, obese, stout, portly
ANTONYMS: slender, lean, spare, gaunt, emaciated

5. disavow
(dis ə vaủ′)

(*v.*) to deny responsibility for or connection with

The suspect stubbornly continued to _____ any part in the kidnapping plot.

SYNONYMS: disclaim, retract, abjure
ANTONYMS: acknowledge, admit, grant, certify

6. dispassionate
(dis pash′ ə nət)

(*adj.*) impartial; calm, free from emotion

Being a neighbor but not quite a family friend, he was called in to give a _____ view of our plan.

SYNONYMS: unbiased, disinterested, cool, detached
ANTONYMS: committed, engaged, partial, biased

7. dissension
(di sen′ shən)

(*n.*) disagreement, sharp difference of opinion

The political party was torn by _____ and finally split into two wings.

SYNONYMS: strife, discord, contention
ANTONYMS: agreement, accord, harmony

8. dissipate
(dis′ ə pāt)

(*v.*) to cause to disappear; to scatter, dispel; to spend foolishly, squander; to be extravagant in pursuit of pleasure

As chairman he is fair and open, but he _____ his energies on trivial things.

SYNONYMS: disperse, strew, diffuse, waste
ANTONYMS: gather, collect, conserve, husband

9. expurgate
(ek′ spər gāt)

(*v.*) to remove objectionable passages or words from a written text; to cleanse, purify

According to the unwritten law of journalism, the editor alone has the right to _____ the article.

SYNONYMS: purge, censor, bowdlerize

10. gauntlet
(gônt′ lət)

(*n.*) an armored or protective glove; a challenge; two lines of men armed with weapons with which to beat a person forced to run between them; an ordeal

In the Middle Ages, a knight threw down his _____ as a challenge, and another knight picked it up only if he accepted.

SYNONYMS: dare, provocation, trial, punishment

11. hypothetical
(hī pə thet′ ə kəl)

(*adj.*) based on an assumption or guess; used as a provisional or tentative idea to guide or direct investigation

Science is not based on _____ assumptions, but on proven facts.

SYNONYMS: assumed, supposed, conditional
ANTONYMS: actual, real, tested, substantiated

12. ignoble
(ig nō′ bəl)

(*adj.*) mean, low, base

Most people will agree that a noble purpose does not justify _____ means.

SYNONYMS: inferior, unworthy, sordid
ANTONYMS: admirable, praiseworthy, lofty, noble

13. impugn
(im pyün′)

(*v.*) to call into question; to attack as false

You can _____ the senator's facts, but you cannot accuse her of concealing her intentions.

SYNONYMS: challenge, deny, dispute, query, question
ANTONYMS: confirm, prove, verify, validate

14. intemperate
(in tem′ pər ət)

(*adj.*) immoderate, lacking in self-control; inclement

Experience taught her to control her _____ outbursts of anger.

SYNONYMS: excessive, extreme, unrestrained, inordinate
ANTONYMS: moderate, restrained, cool and collected

15. odium
(ō′ dē əm)

(*n.*) hatred, contempt; disgrace or infamy resulting from hateful conduct

Those eager to heap _____ on the fallen tyrant learned that he had escaped in the night.

SYNONYMS: abhorrence, opprobrium, shame, ignominy
ANTONYMS: esteem, admiration, approbation

16. perfidy
(pər′ fə dē)

(*n.*) faithlessness, treachery

Rulers in Shakespeare's plays often find themselves armed against enemies but not against the _____ of their friends.

SYNONYMS: betrayal, disloyalty, treason
ANTONYMS: faithfulness, loyalty, steadfastness

17. relegate
(rel′ ə gāt)

(*v.*) to place in a lower position; to assign, refer, turn over; to banish

Even if they _____ him to a mere clerical job, he is determined to make his presence felt.

SYNONYMS: transfer, consign, demote, exile
ANTONYMS: promote, elevate, advance, recall

18. squeamish
(skwē′ mish)

(*adj.*) inclined to nausea; easily shocked or upset; excessively fastidious or refined

If I am called _____ for disliking the horror movie, what do we call those who say that they liked it?

SYNONYMS: nauseated, queasy, delicate, oversensitive, priggish

19. subservient
(səb sər′ vē ənt)

(*adj.*) subordinate in capacity or role; submissively obedient; serving to promote some end

The officers were taught to be respectful of but not blindly _____ to their superior's wishes.

SYNONYMS: secondary, servile, obsequious, useful
ANTONYMS: primary, principal, bossy, domineering

20. susceptible
(sə sep′ tə bəl)

(*adj.*) open to; easily influenced; lacking in resistance

The trouble with being _____ to flattery is that you can never be sure that the flatterer is sincere.

SYNONYMS: vulnerable, receptive, impressionable
ANTONYMS: resistant, immune

Choosing the Right Word

Select the **boldface** word that better completes each sentence. You might refer to the essay on pages 98–99 to see how most of these words are used in context.

1. The (**consternation, dissension**) between Athena and Poseidon led to a contest between the two immortals, in which they bestowed gifts to the Athenians.

2. Though I was annoyed by the child's behavior, the father's outburst of anger seemed to me deplorably (**intemperate, bovine**).

3. The retiring coach said he no longer had the stomach to run the (**gauntlet, odium**) of critics who assailed him after every loss.

4. After the sun set, red and purple hues lingered in the sky for several minutes before the colors (**relegated, dissipated**).

Athena and Poseidon competed to be the patron deity of Athens.

5. If we are going to be required to perform a(n) (**relegated, expurgated**) version of the play, then I think it is not worth doing.

6. I always look for the exit signs in a theater because, (**hypothetically, intemperately**) speaking, one should always be prepared to act in an emergency.

7. My Spanish friend finds it hard to understand the (**odium, perfidy**) attached to bullfighting in most non-Hispanic countries.

8. When Mr. Krummer saw my pathetically inept efforts to prepare a banana split, I was (**impugned, relegated**) to the ranks of the unemployed.

9. Far from being (**ignoble, dispassionate**), her failure after making a valiant effort may serve as an inspiration to young people.

10. The immediate success of my book caused great (**perfidy, consternation**) to my sister, who thinks she is the writer in the family.

11. Students who have been well trained in the social sciences should not be (**susceptible, ignoble**) to the cheap fallacies of racism.

12. Try your best to subdue your natural reluctance and make a (**squeamish, dispassionate**) decision that will be in your son's best interests.

13. Aren't you going a little far when you accuse me of (**consternation, perfidy**) because I didn't vote for you in the beauty contest?

14. Their (**bovine, susceptible**) stares and obvious inability to understand the seriousness of the situation made me doubt their mental capacity.

15. I am not ordinarily a (**corpulent, squeamish**) person, but the sight of that terrible automobile accident haunted me for weeks.

16. A certain amount of disagreement is healthy in any organization, but in our club (**dissension, perfidy**) has almost become a way of life.

17. It is not for me to (**expurgate, impugn**) his motives, but how could anyone, except an overambitious scoundrel, have misled his friends in that way?

18. The prisoner attempted to (**disavow, dissipate**) his confession on the grounds that he had not been informed of his legal rights.

19. There is often a thin line between the kind of debate that is spirited and useful and that which is (**acrimonious, hypothetical**) and nonproductive.

20. Not too long ago in our society, a (**corpulent, bovine**) body was generally admired as a sign of prosperity and physical vigor.

21. The estate he had inherited from his father was (**dissipated, disavowed**) in a long series of impractical and/or mismanaged business enterprises.

22. Imagine our (**consternation, dissension**) when the brakes failed, and we headed full speed toward the busy intersection!

23. By reference to (**ignoble, hypothetical**) cases, you may be able to clarify the difference between "murder" and "manslaughter" for the law students.

24. I noticed with some distaste how her usually overbearing manner became (**susceptible, subservient**) when our employer joined the group.

25. I refuse to ride a roller coaster; fast rides make me (**squeamish, acrimonious**).

Synonyms

*Choose the word from this unit that is the same or most nearly the same in meaning as the **boldface** word or expression in the phrase. Write that word on the line. Use a dictionary if necessary.*

1. their **mindless**, faithful devotion _____

2. to **disown** any credit for herself _____

3. his **caustic** way of speaking _____

4. **take issue with** his credentials _____

5. setting aside her **conjectural** motive _____

6. the brutal **contest** he endured _____

7. a **dishonorable** end to a shadowy life _____

8. feeling **woozy** at the very thought _____

9. **downgraded** to coach seating _____

10. not a hint of **duplicity** in him _____

Antonyms

*Choose the word from this unit that is most nearly opposite in meaning to the **boldface** word or expression in the phrase. Write that word on the line. Use a dictionary if necessary.*

1. a **friendly** game of basketball   _____

2. one of the king's **gallant** knights   _____

3. a gesture of **commitment**   _____

4. listening to a **lively** speech   _____

5. feeling **robust** in the face of adversity   _____

Completing the Sentence

From the words in this unit, choose the one that best completes each of the following sentences. Write the word in the space provided.

1. Far from presenting a unified front, the party is torn by all kinds of strife and

   _____.

2. People with a tendency toward being _____ must wage a lifelong struggle against rich foods.

3. Although she seems rather plodding in her behavior and rarely becomes excited, I think it is unfair to call her "_____."

4. Because Vidkun Quisling cooperated with the Nazis, his name has become a symbol of _____ in his home country of Norway.

5. Our discussion that day was a(n) _____ one, based on the possibility—still far from definite—that I would take the job.

6. Under the American form of government, all branches of the military are clearly _____ to the civilian authority.

7. We have had enough of high-powered, excited oratory; what we need now is a(n) _____ examination of the facts.

8. Anyone as _____ as that trainee will have trouble accustoming himself or herself to the sights, sounds, and smells of hospital work.

9. Now that these ugly facts about his business dealings have come to light, I must _____ my support of his candidacy.

10. The job of cleaning up the field and the stands after the big game was _____ to the freshmen.

11. She is a person of such fine moral standards that she seems incapable of a(n) _____ act.

12. The bold candidate threw down the _____ and dared her opponent to face her in a televised debate.

13. Thomas Bowdler _____ certain words from Shakespeare's plays because he felt that they were unfit to "be read aloud in a family."

14. Instead of using all their forces in one concerted attack on the enemy, they _____ their strength in minor engagements.

15. He is so _____ to flattery that with a few complimentary words I can get him to do almost anything I want.

16. Vigorous debate is fine, but is there any real need for such unrestrained and _____ name-calling?

17. The _____ for this tragic failure does not belong to any individual or small group but to the community as a whole.

18. Though her overall position seemed to be sensible, her language was so unrestrained and _____ that people wouldn't support her.

19. To the _____ of the people in the stands, the lion leaped out of the cage and bounded toward the exit.

20. I am not trying to _____ his truthfulness, but I still do not see how the facts support his claims.

Writing: Words in Action

1. Look back at "Mythical Journeys" (pages 98–99). Imagine that you are Christopher Columbus, and write a letter to your patrons in Spain explaining that, on your voyages, you have not come across any evidence that supports Sir John Mandeville's fanciful claims about strange creatures. Express your disappointment, but reassure your patrons that your voyage still has value for other reasons. Use at least two details from the passage and three unit words.

2. Think about a present-day tale or superstition that some people seem to accept as true but that seems far-fetched to you. (Think of "urban legends" about strange creatures like the chupacabra and Bigfoot, stories of alien encounters, anecdotes about strange or haunted places, and other tales you may have encountered in the media.) Write a brief essay in which you describe one of these tales, speculate about its origins and why it persists, and explain why it is unlikely to be true. Support your essay with specific details, your observations and studies, and the reading (pages 98–99). Write at least three paragraphs, and use three or more words from this unit.

Vocabulary in Context

The following excerpts are from The Wings of the Dove *by Henry James. Some of the words you have studied in this unit appear in* **boldface** *type. Complete each statement below the excerpt by circling the letter of the correct answer.*

1. Thus was kept before him the question of whether it were more **ignoble** to ask a woman to take her chance with you, or to accept it from one's conscience that her chance could be at the best but one of the degrees of privation....

    An **ignoble** gesture is NOT
    a. repugnant
    b. dignified
    c. shameful
    d. dishonorable

2. It might have been a lesson, for our young American, in the art of seeing things as they were—a lesson so various and so sustained that the pupil had...but receptively to gape. The odd thing furthermore was that it could serve its purpose while explicitly **disavowing** every personal bias.

    The act of **disavowing** involves
    a. renouncing
    b. confirming
    c. conjecturing
    d. describing

The Wings of the Dove is a tale about an ailing heiress, Milly Theale, a love triangle, and a devious plan.

3. The one stray gleam of comedy just now in his daughter's eyes was the funny feeling he momentarily made her have of being herself "looked up" by him in sordid lodgings. For a minute after he came in it was as if the place were her own and he the visitor with **susceptibilities**.

    A person with **susceptibilities** is most likely to be
    a. argumentative
    b. serene
    c. confident
    d. vulnerable

4. ...[H]e would stay in spite of her, stay in spite of **odium**, stay in spite perhaps of some final experience that would be, for the pain of it, all but unbearable.

    A person in a state of **odium** feels
    a. happiness
    b. acceptance
    c. boredom
    d. loathing

5. It was as if the drama—it thus came to him, for the fact of a drama there was no blinking—was between *them*, them quite preponderantly; with Merton Densher **relegated** to mere spectatorship, a paying place in front, and one of the most expensive.

    A person who is **relegated** has been
    a. judged
    b. consigned
    c. promoted
    d. assisted

Snap the code, or go to **vocabularyworkshop.com**

*Read the following selection, taking note of the **boldface** words and their contexts. These words are among those you will be studying in Unit 9. As you complete the exercises in this unit, it may help to refer to the way the words are used below.*

The Swedish Nightingale
<Narrative Nonfiction>

The Swedish singer Jenny Lind (1820–1887) was just a **novice** when she made her operatic debut in Stockholm at the age of eighteen. But fame and fortune soon followed, as she quickly went on to enjoy the **adulation** of audiences throughout Europe and, eventually, across the globe. Given that she was one of the first international celebrities, with a major career that lasted for decades and made her a very rich woman, it seems almost **egregious** that few people today have ever heard of Jenny Lind. Yet, as so many celebrated names prove over time, fame is fleeting.

Jenny Lind

Lind possessed a voice so beautiful, and a name so recognizable in Europe, that wherever she performed concert halls quickly sold out. Thus it was not surprising that, after hearing of her many triumphs abroad, the legendary American showman P. T. Barnum proposed to Lind that she tour the United States. Lind did not **equivocate**, for such a tour would provide the opportunity to fund her many charities. However, the singer was as wise as she was talented, and negotiated a contract on terms that were as favorable to her as to Barnum: For 150 concerts over an eighteen-month period, Lind wanted $250,000—a huge sum for the time (about $5 million today). The tour made Lind very wealthy, but despite such earnings, her name was never associated with **avarice**; for Lind devoted much of her accumulated wealth to philanthropic causes, particularly schools, hospitals, and orphanages. Given the singer's generosity, no one would entertain the **supposition** that Lind was **torpid** in aiding the less fortunate. She had not been born into **penury**, yet she had an intuitive sympathy for the poor.

Before her marriage in 1852, Lind was linked romantically to some of the most celebrated figures in the art circles of her day, including the composers Frédéric

M'LLE JENNY LIND'S
NINTH GRAND
CONCERT.
MONDAY, MAY 26.
PARQUETTE.
No. 832

TAKE NOTICE.
This Ticket must be retained, to secure possession of the Seat bearing a corresponding number, which will be shown by the Ushers in attendance. Sit with your back to the number. The Ticket accompanying this is to be given up at the entrance. All persons should be in their seats before the Concert commences.

P. T. Barnum

Van Norden & Amerman. Printers, 60 Wm St.

Ticket for Jenny Lind's New York concert on May 26, 1851

Chopin and Felix Mendelssohn, as well as the writer Hans Christian Andersen, who wrote a fairy tale called "The Nightingale" that was inspired by the singer. Thereafter, Lind was often called "the Swedish Nightingale." She also inspired one of Mendelssohn's masterpieces, the oratorio *Elijah*. Despite such tributes and great fame, Lind was not **pretentious**, arrogant, or conceited; no one who met her could say she was **culpable** of such boorish behavior.

As for P. T. Barnum's role in Lind's career, it had some notable twists and turns. A prodigiously talented showman, Barnum was the mastermind behind a wide range of events, including concerts, museum exhibitions, and the circuses that still bear his name. Gifted with a masterful sense of public relations, he recognized a fantastic money-making opportunity in Jenny Lind: The Swedish Nightingale would help **resuscitate** Barnum's fortunes. But Lind's representative in the contract negotiations was **astute**: He demanded a large advance payment for the American tour. The idea was **anathema** to Barnum, who was accustomed to dealing with his clients on a pay-as-you-go basis. The showman was hard-pressed to raise the funds, but by nature never **dilatory** when it came to making money, Barnum soon found investors and the tour went forward.

Before the tour, few Americans had heard of Lind. However, Barnum's advertisements spread the word about this "gift from Heaven" so shrewdly that by the time the singer arrived by steamship in New York, Lind had become a household name on this side of the Atlantic, too. A crowd of 40,000 people gathered in lower Manhattan to welcome her. Any misgivings in Barnum's mind that Lind's fame in America would prove **evanescent** must have vanished that day. On tour,

Lind performed in a broad variety of venues, ranging from the grand halls of Washington, D.C., before members of the Supreme Court, to Mammoth Cave in central Kentucky. Wherever she went, the enthusiasm for the singer did not **abate**; if anything, it increased in intensity.

Every biographer who has told the story of the Swedish Nightingale **recapitulates** the many achievements of this nineteenth-century celebrity phenomenon. They all agree that part of Lind's appeal was the extraordinary agility, power, and range of her singing voice. But they point out that Lind's musical talent was enhanced even more by her aura of propriety and refinement. In an era of conservative mores, such a public image was a decided plus for a celebrity performer, and Barnum took full advantage of Lind's squeaky-clean reputation. But with or without Barnum, there was never anything **nebulous** about her fame: From the day she first walked onstage, Jenny Lind had "star power."

Hans Christian Andersen

iWords

Snap the code, or go to **vocabularyworkshop.com**

Definitions

Note the spelling, pronunciation, part(s) of speech, and definition(s) of each of the following words. Then write the word in the blank spaces in the illustrative sentence(s) following. Finally, study the lists of synonyms and antonyms.

1. abate
(ə bāt')

(v.) to make less in amount, degree, etc.; to subside, become less; to nullify; to deduct, omit

We stood on the dock on that moonless night, waiting for the storm to _____.

SYNONYMS: diminish, decrease, subside, let up
ANTONYMS: intensify, increase, magnify, wax

2. adulation
(aj ə lā' shən)

(n.) praise or flattery that is excessive

Athletes have little choice but to enjoy the sometimes puzzling _____ of their fans.

SYNONYMS: adoration, idolization, hero-worship
ANTONYMS: ridicule, derision, odium

3. anathema
(ə nath' ə mə)

(n.) an object of intense dislike; a curse or strong denunciation (often used adjectivally without the article)

The author's views on bringing up children are _____ to my dad but a delight to my mother.

SYNONYMS: malediction, imprecation, abomination
ANTONYMS: benediction, blessing

4. astute
(ə stüt')

(adj.) shrewd, crafty, showing practical wisdom

The _____ management of money is a valuable skill but may not by itself make a good executive.

SYNONYMS: acute, sagacious, judicious, wily
ANTONYMS: obtuse, doltish, empty-headed, dumb

5. avarice
(av' ər is)

(n.) a greedy desire, particularly for wealth

Her career exhibited both the miser's ever-growing _____ and the miser's diminishing charm.

SYNONYMS: cupidity, rapacity, acquisitiveness

6. culpable
(kəl' pə bəl)

(adj.) deserving blame, worthy of condemnation

It was the inspectors' _____ neglect of duty that left such old buses in service.

SYNONYMS: guilty, delinquent, peccant, blameworthy
ANTONYMS: blameless, innocent, laudable, meritorious

7. dilatory
(dil′ ə tôr ē)

(*adj.*) tending to delay or procrastinate; not prompt; intended to delay or postpone

She hired an assistant because, on her own, she was always _____ in paying her bills.

SYNONYMS: stalling, slow, tardy, laggard
ANTONYMS: prompt, punctual, speedy, expeditious

8. egregious
(i grē′ jəs)

(*adj.*) conspicuous, standing out from the mass (used particularly in an unfavorable sense)

Whoever allowed that man on a stage is guilty of an _____ blunder.

SYNONYMS: glaring, flagrant, blatant
ANTONYMS: unnoticeable, paltry, piddling

9. equivocate
(i kwiv′ ə kāt)

(*v.*) to speak or act in a way that allows for more than one interpretation; to be deliberately vague or ambiguous

I won't soon give my vote to a candidate who shows such a marked tendency to _____.

SYNONYMS: to talk out of both sides of one's mouth, palter, hedge
ANTONYM: to speak one's mind plainly

10. evanescent
(ev ə nes′ ənt)

(*adj.*) vanishing, soon passing away; light and airy

Looking back, I see that the magic of that summer was _____.

SYNONYMS: ephemeral, transient, transitory
ANTONYMS: everlasting, immortal, imperishable

11. irresolute
(ir ez′ ə lüt)

(*adj.*) unable to make up one's mind, hesitating

In *Hamlet*, the prince is _____ about whether to obey his father's ghost or to go on as if nothing has happened.

SYNONYMS: indecisive, vacillating, wavering
ANTONYMS: determined, decisive, unwavering

12. nebulous
(neb′ yə ləs)

(*adj.*) cloudlike, resembling a cloud; cloudy in color, not transparent; vague, confused, indistinct

By the time everyone had expressed an opinion, the original idea had become somewhat _____.

SYNONYMS: hazy, fuzzy, cloudy, opaque, indeterminate
ANTONYMS: definite, distinct, clear, sharply focused

13. novice
(näv′ is)

(*n.*) one who is just a beginner at some activity requiring skill and experience (also used adjectivally)

You must be patient and realize that all his mistakes are typical of a _____ in this line of work.

SYNONYMS: neophyte, tyro, trainee, apprentice
ANTONYMS: veteran, past master, pro, expert

14. penury
(pen′ yə rē)

(*n.*) extreme poverty; barrenness, insufficiency

We never seem to tire of stories of people who go from _____ to sudden wealth.

SYNONYMS: destitution, indigence; ANTONYMS: affluence, luxury

15. pretentious
(prē ten′ shəs)

(*adj.*) done for show, striving to make a big impression; claiming merit or position unjustifiably; ambitious

Talking about one's wealth is thought to be _____ and in poor taste.

SYNONYMS: ostentatious, inflated; ANTONYMS: unaffected, modest

16. recapitulate
(rē ka pich′ ə lāt)

(*v.*) to review a series of facts; to sum up

Don't bother to _____ the plot of the book; instead, tell me if you liked it.

SYNONYMS: review, summarize, go over

17. resuscitate
(ri səs′ ə tāt)

(*v.*) to revive, bring back to consciousness or existence

We need someone who can _____ our neighborhood's community spirit.

SYNONYMS: revitalize, reanimate, restore, reactivate

18. slovenly
(sləv′ ən lē)

(*adj.*) untidy, dirty, careless

Her room was in a _____ state, and it took her an entire Saturday to clean it.

SYNONYMS: unkempt, slatternly, lax; ANTONYMS: neat, meticulous

19. supposition
(səp ə zish′ ən)

(*n.*) something that is assumed or taken for granted without conclusive evidence

Guided by a _____ that turned out to be false, they made some disastrous decisions.

SYNONYMS: assumption, presumption, hypothesis

20. torpid
(tôr′ pid)

(*adj.*) inactive, sluggish, dull

We all felt _____ after that long, dull lecture.

SYNONYMS: lethargic, languid; ANTONYMS: energetic, vigorous

Choosing the Right Word

*Select the **boldface** word that better completes each sentence. You might refer to the selection on pages 108–109 to see how most of these words are used in context.*

1. Before becoming a successful writer, Jack London was a (**torpid, novice**) prospector, searching for gold in Alaska.

2. As the election drew nearer, the candidates went from reasonable discussion to quarrelsomeness to (**anathematizing, recapitulating**) each other.

3. Is it any wonder that a 17-year-old star athlete becomes smug when she receives such (**recapitulation, adulation**) from the entire school?

4. Since my mother is such a(n) (**astute, dilatory**) manager, she was the perfect choice to run the children's museum in our community.

Jack London is known for his Alaska stories, such as *The Son of the Wolf* and *The Call of the Wild*.

5. What do you think of the concept that when a crime is committed, society is often as (**culpable, astute**) as the criminal?

6. As a result of (**irresolution, egregiousness**) when that novel was first submitted, the publishing house lost the biggest best seller of the year.

7. The glory of this perfect spring day seems to be all the more precious because it is so (**torpid, evanescent**).

8. I was absolutely stunned when I reviewed my bank statement, not realizing I had made an (**irresolute, egregious**) error in accounting.

9. As soon as the hurricane (**abated, equivocated**), rescue teams rushed out to help people in the devastated area.

10. The heat in the room, the quiet drone of the fly at the window, and the bright sunlight put me into a (**torpid, slovenly**) state.

11. Sheila was feeling insecure after experiencing a (**culpable, nebulous**) sense of dread that something terrible was going to happen during her speech.

12. Biologists have a theory that every plant or animal in the course of its development (**abates, recapitulates**) all the stages of its evolution.

13. Since he is known to be a multimillionaire, it seems almost (**culpable, pretentious**) of him, in an inverted sense, to drive around in a small, battered, inexpensive car.

14. You may be right in your belief that she won't let us use her car, but remember that this is still only a(n) (**anathema, supposition**).

15. In the densely populated and underdeveloped countries we visited, we saw the depths to which people can be reduced by (**penury, anathema**).

16. He is completely indifferent to wealth and luxurious living; his (**anathema, avarice**) is directed instead toward fame and prestige.

17. In playing chess, she deliberately uses (**dilatory, nebulous**) tactics to make her opponent impatient and tense.

18. When the results of her mistakes became public knowledge, she gained a well-deserved reputation for being an (**astute, egregious**) blunderer.

19. Only a (**penury, novice**) at golf would have tried to use a driver when hitting into such a strong wind.

20. In everyone's life, a situation may arise that calls for a basic moral choice to be made, without compromise or (**abatement, equivocation**).

21. The (**slovenly, pretentious**) physical appearance of the report was matched by its careless writing and disorganized content.

22. Sportswriters attribute the success of the pennant-winning team largely to the (**astute, evanescent**) managing of old Buck Coakley.

23. What she calls her "philosophy of life" seems to me a hodgepodge of childish fallacies and (**dilatory, nebulous**) generalizations.

24. They say that school spirit at Central High is dead, but I am confident that it can be (**resuscitated, equivocated**) if the right methods are used.

25. It is difficult to remember my dreams, as I find them to be (**evanescent, astute**).

 **Synonyms**

*Choose the word from this unit that is the same or most nearly the same in meaning as the **boldface** word or expression in the phrase. Write that word on the line. Use a dictionary if necessary.*

1. **dithering** over a choice   _____

2. guilty of **brazen** rudeness   _____

3. a delicate and **fleeting** beauty   _____

4. **restate** your requirements   _____

5. ashamed of a **slipshod** job   _____

6. **prevaricated** about the true amount   _____

7. **breathe new life into** the dull party   _____

8. made **listless** by the heat   _____

9. a maddeningly **murky** explanation   _____

10. a muttered **execration**   _____

Antonyms

*Choose the word from this unit that is most nearly opposite in meaning to the **boldface** word or expression in the phrase. Write that word on the line. Use a dictionary if necessary.*

1. their **subtle** errors   _____

2. a **well-groomed and careful** dresser   _____

3. closing with a **word of approval**   _____

4. an experienced and **tenacious** nanny   _____

5. the presentation of a **fully defined** concept _____

Completing the Sentence

From the words in this unit, choose the one that best completes each of the following sentences. Write the word in the space provided.

1. Using the most up-to-date equipment, the firefighters worked tirelessly to _____ the victim of smoke inhalation.

2. I don't think I'd call such a(n) _____ grammatical mistake a minor "slip of the pen."

3. I was so _____ about whether to go out for basketball or for swimming that I ended up going out for neither.

4. When you are _____ in returning a book to the library, you are preventing someone else from using it.

5. As her anger slowly _____, she realized that such childish outbursts of emotion would do nothing to help solve her problems.

6. It will mean more to him to gain the approval of the few people who can appreciate his work than to receive the _____ of the crowd.

7. I told my friend that dress for the party was casual, but he showed up looking, in my opinion, just plain _____.

8. How can you consider him _____ when the accident was caused by a landslide that no one could have foreseen or prevented?

9. Since I truly loathe people who think they are "above the common herd," any form of snobbery is absolutely _____ to me.

10. The study of history teaches us that a hunger for land, like other kinds of _____, is the cause of a great many wars.

11. He holds forth in great detail on what is wrong with our city government, but the remedies he suggests are exceedingly _____.

12. The _____ she had experienced in her childhood and youth made her keenly aware of the value of money.

13. Since he was a(n) _____ at the game, the three veteran players hoped to find someone more suitable to play on their team.

14. Your brilliant plan is based on one false _____—that I am willing to work without pay.

15. Does he use all those quotations as a means of clarifying his meaning, or simply as a(n) _____ display of his learning?

16. Sure, it's great to be a big-league ballplayer, but bear in mind that the years of stardom are brief and _____.

17. I was impressed by the _____ way our hostess guided the conversation away from topics that might be embarrassing to her guests.

18. After giving us extremely detailed instructions for more than an hour, she briefly _____ and then sent us out on our assignments.

19. Although she tried to _____, we insisted on a simple "yes" or "no" answer.

20. Her mind, _____ as a result of hours of exposure to the bitter cold, was not alert enough to sense the impending danger.

Writing: Words in Action

1. Look back at "The Swedish Nightingale" (pages 108–109). Suppose you have been hired by P. T. Barnum to promote an upcoming concert by Jenny Lind in a major American city. Write a press release to persuade people to attend the event. Use at least two details from the passage and three unit words.

2. ...[M]usical training is a more potent instrument than any other, because rhythm and harmony find their way into the inward places of the soul, on which they mightily fasten, imparting grace....—Plato, from The Republic

Music is an integral part of life; people listen to it everywhere, spend money on it, play it, and find inspiration in it. Write a speech in which you argue in support of music education. What, in your opinion, are the most compelling reasons for making music a part of every person's basic education? Support your essay with specific details, your observations and studies, and the reading (pages 108–109). Write at least three paragraphs, and use three or more words from this unit.

Vocabulary in Context

The following excerpts are from The House of Mirth *by Edith Wharton. Some of the words you have studied in this unit appear in* **boldface** *type. Complete each statement below the excerpt by circling the letter of the correct answer.*

1. Lily sat down beside the desk at the foot of her bed, and spreading out the check, read over and over the TEN THOUSAND DOLLARS written across it in a steely business hand. Ten months earlier the amount it stood for had represented the depths of **penury**; but her standard of values had changed in the interval, and now visions of wealth lurked in every flourish of the pen.

Being in a state of **penury** suggests

a. indigence   **c.** affluence
b. euphoria   **d.** insolence

2. He had the dull man's unexpected flashes of **astuteness**, and Lily could not help joining in the laugh with which he had pounced on the truth.

A person displaying **astuteness** is

a. juvenile   **c.** inconsiderate
b. suspicious   **d.** perceptive

3. But the hour sped on and Selden did not come. Doubtless he had been detained, or had misread her hurriedly scrawled note, taking the four for a five. The ringing of the door-bell a few minutes after five confirmed this **supposition**...

A **supposition** is a(n)

a. yearning   **c.** delusion
b. conclusion   **d.** inaccuracy

The House of Mirth examines the role of women and high society in New York at the turn of the nineteenth century.

4. "Oh, thank you: I'm not particularly well, but Miss Haines was right. I AM clumsy."

"Well, it's mean work for anybody with a headache." Miss Kilroy paused **irresolutely**. "You ought to go right home and lay down..."

If a person pauses **irresolutely**, he or she acts with

a. hesitation   **c.** authority
b. resolve   **d.** refinement

5. Her loudly affirmed pleasure at seeing Miss Bart took the form of a **nebulous** generalization, which included neither enquiries as to her future nor the expression of a definite wish to see her again.

A **nebulous** impression is NOT

a. distant   **c.** precise
b. indistinct   **d.** vague

Interactive Quiz

Snap the code, or go to **vocabularyworkshop.com**

Vocabulary for Comprehension

*Read the following selection in which some of the words you have studied in Units 7–9 appear in **boldface** type. Then answer the questions on page 119.*

This passage discusses some aspects of elephants' behavior, especially the ways in which they communicate.

(Line)

At first look, the counting of elephants would seem no harder than the counting of slow-moving trucks. But garnering information
(5) about the population density of elephants has proved to be no easy task for scientists from Cornell University. It is believed that half of the close-knit elephant families in
(10) Southern Africa live in dense and tangled forests, and counting these **corpulent** creatures raises several interesting questions.

A full-grown elephant must eat 500
(15) pounds of leaves a day. This means that family members, though deeply devoted, spend much time apart— far apart, so as not to **pillage** one another's lunch. How do they keep in
(20) touch? And how many humans would it take to hack through a jungle trying to count an unknown number of widely separated subjects?

Fortunately, these royal families of
(25) the southern forest do keep in touch, and not only by the high-pitched, trumpetlike blasts we've heard in the movies. Some years ago, scientists discovered that elephants also make
(30) sounds too deep for human ears to detect. Although these rumblings are apparently **nebulous**, they are not **inconsequential** in meaning. They

seem to keep widely scattered family
(35) members moving in the same direction and headed toward the same destination. They also seem to signal comfort to a strayed elephant calf whose elders are coming to
(40) retrieve it. While the high-pitched call is absorbed by trees or **dissipated** into the air, the deep call is able to travel much greater distances. Are these low rumblings a sophisticated
(45) form of communication, or even language? The Cornell team hopes to find out.

Meanwhile, the scientists mount recording devices in many parts of
(50) the forest, converting the inaudible elephant sounds to visual signs on computer disks. The team determines how long each call took to reach each recorder and
(55) eventually charts both the number of elephants in an area and the course of their movements.

As for decoding the calls, this process may be greatly helped when
(60) cameras join the recording devices in the forest. Researchers hope that when they **recapitulate** both the "soundless" calls and the visual records of the elephants' actions,
(65) clues will emerge as to what these sociable creatures are saying.

1. The primary purpose of the passage is to explain
   a. that elephants possess language
   b. the obstacles to an accurate census of elephants
   c. that elephants are endangered
   d. how animal behavior experts employ sophisticated technology
   e. how members of elephant families keep in touch in dense forests

2. According to the passage, counting elephants is difficult because of
   a. their shyness
   b. their habitat
   c. their eating habits
   d. their aggressiveness
   e. their resemblance to one another

3. The meaning of **corpulent** (line 12) is
   a. portly
   b. sociable
   c. invisible
   d. affectionate
   e. long-lived

4. The writer includes the rhetorical question in lines 20–23 to show
   a. his expertise on the topic
   b. that no current census is accurate
   c. how hard it is to count elephants
   d. that elephants are poorly understood
   e. that humans may not have the ability to survive in a dense forest

5. **Pillage** (line 18) most nearly means
   a. share
   b. loot
   c. step on
   d. spoil
   e. rub against

6. According to the passage, elephants stay in contact by
   a. pulling down large trees at regular intervals
   b. creating large piles of stones
   c. signalling with their trunks
   d. emitting deep rumbling sounds humans cannot hear
   e. scraping bare patches on the forest floor

7. The meaning of **nebulous** (line 32) is
   a. strange
   b. sonorous
   c. surprising
   d. menacing
   e. indistinct

8. **Inconsequential** (line 33) is best defined as
   a. trivial
   b. frequent
   c. pleasant
   d. important
   e. unfriendly

9. Which of the following statements can be inferred from the passage?
   a. Elephants are loners by nature.
   b. Elephants live in close-knit groups.
   c. Elephant numbers are declining in Southern Africa.
   d. Elephants make deep rumbling sounds to frighten away predators.
   e. Elephants are migrating from dense forests to more open habitats.

10. **Dissipated** (line 41) most nearly means
    a. blocked
    b. enhanced
    c. diffused
    d. corrupted
    e. mixed up

11. **Recapitulate** (line 62) is best defined as
    a. reorganize
    b. preserve
    c. record
    d. match
    e. review

12. In the passage, the author's perspective is that of a(n)
    a. fundraiser for wildlife conservation
    b. science writer
    c. expert in animal behavior
    d. interested amateur
    e. science teacher

Two-Word Completions

Select the pair of words that best complete the meaning of each of the following passages.

1. The _____ of history forever attaches itself to the name of Benedict Arnold for his villainous act of _____ during the American Revolution.
   a. acrimony . . . beneficence
   b. odium . . . perfidy
   c. consternation . . . equivocation
   d. anathema . . . restitution

2. A person has to have a strong stomach to work in a funeral parlor or morgue. Handling _____ is definitely not a job for the

   _____ .

   a. stalwarts . . . slovenly
   b. novices . . . redoubtable
   c. cadavers . . . squeamish
   d. concoctions . . . acrimonious

3. Though a few lucky "haves" are able to provide themselves with all the comforts of life on a truly _____ scale, the bulk of the people in many third-world countries seem to live like paupers in the most extreme state of _____ and neglect.
   a. egregious . . . avarice
   b. punctilious . . . dissension
   c. redoubtable . . . perfidy
   d. grandiose . . . penury

4. For a minor _____ of the rules of a hockey game, the offending player is _____ to the penalty box, or "sin bin," for two minutes. For a more serious violation, he is put there for five.
   a. anathema . . . recapitulated
   b. infraction . . . relegated
   c. supposition . . . disavowed
   d. dissension . . . debased

5. In AD 267, a band of barbarous Heruli raided the ancient Greek religious center at Delphi. For several days they _____ the town and _____ its temples. Then they rode off, laden with plunder.
   a. relegated . . . dissipated
   b. resuscitated . . . debased
   c. pillaged . . . desecrated
   d. disconcerted . . . expurgated

6. "Those who circumvent the law are often as _____ as those who actually break it," the lawyer remarked. "The seriousness of such an offense is rarely _____ by the fact that, technically, no crime has been committed."
   a. culpable . . . mitigated
   b. corpulent . . . abated
   c. vulnerable . . . impugned
   d. susceptible . . . disavowed

7. His kindness may have been a(n) _____ act, performed in a moment of distraction, but its _____ impact on the young orphans caused them to grow up and pursue careers as social workers.
   a. vulnerable . . . astute
   b. pretentious . . . egregious
   c. inconsequential . . . beneficent
   d. susceptible . . . intemperate

Idioms

In the essay "An Overlooked Exploration" (see pages 88–89), the author states that Charles Wilkes "got his just deserts" when he returned from his expedition. To get one's "just deserts" (*deserts* is pronounced like *desserts* but means "a reward or punishment that is deserved") means to receive retribution for one's actions.

Phrases such as "just deserts" are idioms. **Idioms** are phrases or expressions that usually have a meaning different from the one that the individual words suggest. Idioms are figures of speech, expressions that are not to be taken literally. Many idioms are clever and colorful, and people say them so often that they do not even realize they are using them. Though the meaning of some idioms can be determined from context clues, others are not quite as obvious and have to be learned.

Choosing the Right Idiom

Read each sentence. Use context clues to figure out the meaning of each idiom in **boldface** *print. Then write the letter of the definition for the idiom in the sentence.*

1. I'm so glad the president kept her speech **short and sweet**. _____

2. I wish Dad would just **cut to the chase** and tell me if I can borrow the car or not. _____

3. The new song I'm learning is **a piece of cake**, so I should be able to play it tomorrow. _____

4. Bob has been campaigning for Senator Jones, but I think he is **backing the wrong horse**. _____

5. I wouldn't trust Megan; she is pretty good at using **crocodile tears** to get her way. _____

6. We decided to ask Leroy to join our team because he is great at **thinking on his feet**. _____

7. Tomas will be in for **a rude awakening** when he gets his own apartment and has to cook and clean for himself! _____

8. You left too early and missed the amazing encore. The band **brought the house down**! _____

9. My mother sent me out **on a wild goose chase** to find decorations for my sister's birthday party. _____

10. I'm not surprised your company went bankrupt after you told me they had been **cooking the books**. _____

a. leave out the details and get to the point

b. fake sadness used to manipulate people

c. an unpleasant understanding or revelation

d. a wasted effort looking for something that is difficult to find or nonexistent

e. making decisions with little effort or prior planning

f. put on a successful performance

g. something easy; a task that can be completed without much effort

h. manipulating financial figures

i. brief yet meaningful; direct and to the point

j. supporting the wrong or losing side

Writing with Idioms

Find the meaning of each idiom. (Use an online or print dictionary if necessary.) Then write a sentence for each idiom.

1. cast a wide net

_____

2. take it with a grain of salt

_____

3. walking on eggshells

_____

4. blow a fuse

_____

5. on your high horse

_____

_____

6. herding cats

_____

_____

7. dial it back

_____

_____

8. common ground

_____

9. a drop in the ocean

_____

10. a feather in your cap

_____

11. give up the ghost

_____

12. a fly on the wall

_____

Denotation and Connotation

When you look for the definition of a word, you search for the word's **denotation**, or its formal meaning. A denotation is neutral and objective. A word may also have a **connotation**, or an implied meaning that people commonly associate with it. These implied meanings can be either positive or negative.

Consider these synonyms for the word *acrimonious.*

> *cantankerous   belligerent   vicious   ruthless*

Cantankerous and *belligerent* **have negative connotations,** referring to aggressive, unfriendly behaviors. *Vicious* and *ruthless* have even more negative connotations, referring to brutally cruel behaviors. The different shades of meaning in these words mean that they cannot be used interchangeably; there are differences in their intensity and in the way they are perceived by a listener or reader.

> **Think:** An angry, unhappy person can sometimes be *cantankerous* or *belligerent*, but only a truly heartless person is *vicious* and *ruthless*.

Look at these examples of words. Notice how the connotation of each word varies.

NEUTRAL	POSITIVE	NEGATIVE
grand	majestic	grandiose
notable	illustrious	redoubtable
intelligent	astute	wily

To use language effectively, a writer needs to be mindful of how words convey subtle shades of meaning. Using the wrong word can send the wrong message. Imagine a restaurant owner getting ready to print his menu. He knows that customers will react differently to *calamari* versus *fried squid*. Which would you order?

Shades of Meaning

Write a plus sign (+) in the box if the word has a positive connotation. Write a minus sign (−) if the word has a negative connotation. Put a zero (0) if the word is neutral.

1. odium ☐   **2.** beneficent ☐   **3.** austere ☐   **4.** hypothetical ☐

5. dissipated ☐   **6.** torpid ☐   **7.** corpulent ☐   **8.** avarice ☐

9. stalwart ☐   **10.** desecrate ☐   **11.** restitution ☐   **12.** resuscitate ☐

13. mitigate ☐   **14.** gauntlet ☐   **15.** squeamish ☐   **16.** nebulous ☐

Expressing the Connotation

Read each sentence. Select the word in parentheses that expresses the connotation (positive, negative, or neutral) given at the beginning of the sentence.

negative   **1.** We do not like to leave my grandmother home alone very much, as she is quite (**vulnerable, powerless**).

positive   **2.** Eliot is the best person to serve as a mediator, since he can be counted on to be (**dispassionate, disinterested**) in his judgments.

neutral   **3.** Though Katie is a (**novice, rookie**) at running, she finished the 5K run in under twenty-five minutes.

negative   **4.** My tennis coach (**cautioned, reproved**) me, saying I stoop too much while playing.

positive   **5.** When the peasant (**queried, impugned**) the king's taxes, he was placed in the pillory.

negative   **6.** Don't you consider it (**anathema, rudeness**) when people talk loudly on their cell phones in public?

positive   **7.** Ever the (**subservient, dutiful**) entertainer, King Lear's fool also serves as the King's conscience.

neutral   **8.** I was furious when Aunt Helen (**relegated, assigned**) me to sit at the children's table.

Challenge: Using Connotation

Choose vocabulary words from Units 7–9 to replace the highlighted words in the sentences below. Then explain how the connotation of the replacement word changes the tone of the sentence.

susceptible	**concoct**	**recapitulating**
pillaging	**ignoble**	**mitigate**

1. My mother likes to **make** _____ her own soothing liquids that can be used to alleviate insect bites.

_____

_____

2. Upon landing on the island, the adventurers began **robbing** _____ the village.

_____

_____

3. The general enacted **shameful** _____ laws that restricted people's rights and freedoms.

_____

_____

Classical Roots

mor—form, shape;
the—to put or place

The root *mor* appears in **amorphous** (page 52), "shapeless, without definite form." The root *the* appears in **anathema** (page 110), meaning "an object of intense dislike." Some other words based on these roots are listed below.

anthropomorphic	metamorphosis	morphology	pseudomorph
epithet	parenthetical	theme	thesis

From the list of words above, choose the one that corresponds to each of the brief definitions below. Write the word in the blank space in the illustrative sentence below the definition. Use an online or print dictionary if necessary.

1. contained in parenthesis; qualifying or explanatory

She made a few _____ remarks before starting her speech.

2. a proposition that is put forth for argument

The professor offered evidence in support of her _____.

3. the study of form and structure

Students of biological _____ analyze animal forms.

4. a false, deceptive, or irregular form

Scientists are seldom fooled by a(n) _____.

5. a marked change, a transformation

The child was amazed by the _____ of the caterpillar.

6. characterized by the attribution of human qualities to nonhuman phenomena

Giving pets human names is a common _____ practice.

7. a topic of discourse or discussion; an idea, point of view

The _____ of the essay was the misuse of technology.

8. a term used to characterize the nature of a person or thing

"The King" is the _____ used by Elvis fans for their hero.

*Read the following selection, taking note of the **boldface** words and their contexts. These words are among those you will be studying in Unit 10. As you complete the exercises in this unit, it may help to refer to the way the words are used below.*

Sinking Nation

<Magazine Article>

It sounds like a tropical paradise, with a **munificent** bounty of natural attractions: sun-bleached beaches, turquoise waters, swaying coconut palm trees, breathtaking sunsets. But the tiny South Pacific nation of Tuvalu is sinking, and its inhabitants are threatened and cannot afford to **procrastinate**: Unless drastic measures are taken, climate experts predict that Tuvalu could disappear in under fifty years.

Located halfway between Australia and Hawaii, Tuvalu is an archipelago made up of nine small, low-lying reef islands and atolls. A former British protectorate, it gained independence in 1978 and United Nations membership in 2000. With a population of about 10,000 and encompassing a total land area of ten square miles, Tuvalu is the fourth-smallest country in the world (only Monaco, Vatican City, and Tuvalu's South Pacific neighbor, Nauru, are smaller).

Over time, earthquakes, tsunamis, cyclones, and hurricanes have caused erosion and taken a toll. But the more recent—and dangerous—sea-level rise is attributed to the catastrophic effects of global warming. The islands and atolls of Tuvalu offer no **coverts** where people can escape the sea.

The world first became aware of the scope of the crisis at the 1997 Kyoto Conference, which was convened to address climate change. The timing of the conference was **fortuitous**. Before then, Tuvaluans had viewed the issue with **equanimity**; they adjusted to rising sea levels by moving farther and farther inland. Naysayers who deny climate change is to blame assert that the **provocative** claims of the islanders are overblown. And facts and figures may seem **recondite**, but one fact is clear: The land mass is getting significantly smaller each year, and Tuvalu is being reclaimed by the sea.

The narrow island nation of Tuvalu, in the Pacific Ocean, as seen from the air

Pacific Island leaders meet at the Pacific Islands Forum.

Tuvaluan leaders are hoping to avoid the **bedlam** that their nation faces by finding the most **efficacious** means of solving their problem. So they talk to officials from the United States, Australia, and other major nations and plead for cooperation in capping greenhouse-gas emissions. (Tuvaluan leaders have, at times, received **gratuitous**, even **imperious**, responses. Some insensitive government representatives claim the islanders are to blame for the flooding because of their own poor environmental management.) But actions speak louder than words, and Tuvalu cannot wait.

The people of Tuvalu are poor and lack the financial resources to mount much of a "Save Tuvalu" campaign. The nation is too remote to attract many tourists. Per-capita income is negligible; the islanders survive mostly by fishing and farming the little land they have. (One interesting **annotation**, or side note, to this story: Tuvalu is resorting to Internet Age solutions. Besides publicizing this pressing threat to its existence, the nation has **accrued** significant revenue by leasing the marketing rights to its ".tv" Internet domain name. The deal has brought in millions of dollars that can be invested in projects aimed at alleviating the country's problems.)

Each year, approximately seventy-five natives resettle in New Zealand, and leaders are in talks with other South Pacific nations to take in more people. This slow relocation provokes thorny legal and human-rights issues: Does a country still exist if all its inhabitants leave, deciding that they cannot remain **sedentary** in the face of the encroaching sea? Will Tuvaluans still be Tuvaluans if the ocean swallows their homeland? Can they still be represented at the UN? Can they continue to claim fishing and other ocean rights that bring in much-needed income? The **gist** of the problem is this: Without a man-made miracle, the Tuvaluans' tiny homeland will sink without a trace—thus making it a modern-day Atlantis.

Schoolchildren in Tuvalu

Snap the code, or go to **vocabularyworkshop.com**

Definitions

Note the spelling, pronunciation, part(s) of speech, and definition(s) of each of the following words. Then write the word in the blank spaces in the illustrative sentence(s) following. Finally, study the lists of synonyms and antonyms.

1. accrue
(ə krü′)

(*v.*) to grow or accumulate over time; to happen as a natural result

We allowed the interest to _____ on the account until it turned into a small fortune.

SYNONYMS: collect, accumulate, proceed from
ANTONYMS: dwindle, decrease, diminish, lessen

2. annotation
(an ə tā′ shən)

(*n.*) a critical or explanatory note or comment, especially for a literary work

Laurence Sterne's novel *Tristram Shandy* has almost as many _____ as lines of text.

3. bedlam
(bed′ ləm)

(*n.*) a state or scene of uproar and confusion

Is this the same band that caused mob scenes and virtual _____ on its first tour?

SYNONYMS: commotion, pandemonium, chaos, anarchy
ANTONYMS: peace and quiet, order, tranquility

4. covert
(kō′ vert)
(ko′ vert)

(*adj.*) hidden, disguised, purposefully kept secret; sheltered, secluded; (*n.*) a sheltered place, a hiding place

Napoleon was an expert at making _____ preparations to attack unsuspecting opponents.

The bear made a lunge from her _____ before we realized she was nearby.

SYNONYMS: (*adj.*) undercover, clandestine, sub-rosa
ANTONYMS: (*adj.*) open, overt, undisguised

5. debonair
(deb ə når′)

(*adj.*) pleasant, courteous, lighthearted; smooth and polished in manner and appearance

Quite a few _____ young men asked my cousin to dance.

SYNONYMS: carefree, jaunty, gracious, urbane
ANTONYMS: distraught, agitated, boorish, churlish

6. dun
(dən)

(*v.*) to demand insistently, especially in payment of a debt; (*n.*) a creditor; (*adj.*) dark, dull, drab, dingy

Many of Charles Dickens's characters are _____ by creditors because of their large debts.

SYNONYMS: (*v.*) hound, harass, nag

7. efficacious
(ef ə kā′ shəs)

(*adj.*) effective, producing results

Not the most charming of senators, he nevertheless wielded the most _____ knowledge of statecraft.

SYNONYMS: effectual, efficient, potent, powerful
ANTONYMS: ineffective, worthless, useless

8. equanimity
(ek wə nim′ ə tē)

(*n.*) calmness, composure, refusal to panic

Injustice always sent him into a rage, but he could endure misfortune with _____.

SYNONYMS: tranquility, imperturbability
ANTONYMS: excitability, flappability, agitation

9. fortuitous
(fôr tü′ ə təs)

(*adj.*) accidental, occurring by a happy chance

Due to a _____ drop in oil prices, the shipping company showed healthy profits for the year.

SYNONYMS: unintentional, unplanned, random, lucky
ANTONYMS: intentional, deliberate, premeditated

10. gist
(jist)

(*n.*) the essential part, main point, or essence

Would the talented fellow who keeps the back row in stitches please repeat the _____ of what I said?

SYNONYMS: substance, core, nucleus

11. gratuitous
(grə tü′ ə təs)

(*adj.*) freely given; not called for by circumstances, unwarranted

Though she had hoped to leave the lecture early, several members of the audience asked _____ questions, delaying her by an hour.

SYNONYMS: voluntary, unjustified; ANTONYMS: justified, warranted

12. imperious
(im pir′ ē əs)

(*adj.*) overbearing, arrogant; seeking to dominate; pressing, compelling

The Wizard of Oz's _____ manner masked the reality that he was a fussy little man behind a curtain.

SYNONYMS: domineering, magisterial, urgent, imperative
ANTONYMS: fawning, obsequious, humble, unassuming

13. invective
(in vek′ tiv)

(*n.*) a strong denunciation or condemnation; abusive language; (*adj.*) abusive, vituperative

He let loose his usual hail of _____, a furious shower that left the air a bit clearer.

As _____ speeches go, this one displayed originality, vigor, and, here and there, some wit.

SYNONYMS: (*n.*) vituperation, abuse, philippic
ANTONYMS: (*n.*) tribute, panegyric, encomium

14. motley
(mät' lē)

(*adj.*) showing great variety; composed of different elements or many colors; (*n.*) a jester's costume; a jester

Tall and short, thick and thin, old and young, we share the family name but are a _____ bunch indeed.

To "put on _____" is to say what only a king's jester would dare to say.

SYNONYMS: (*adj.*) variegated, heterogeneous, diverse; (*n.*) fool
ANTONYMS: (*adj.*) homogeneous, monochromatic

15. munificent
(myü nif' ə sənt)

(*adj.*) extremely generous, lavish

Nothing the volunteers said could save the program until our anonymous friend donated a _____ sum.

SYNONYMS: bounteous, liberal; ANTONYMS: miserly, parsimonious

16. procrastinate
(prə kras' tə nāt)

(*v.*) to delay, put off until later

We all want to _____ when a task is no fun, but some people make delaying a way of life.

SYNONYMS: stall, temporize, dillydally

17. provocative
(prə väk' ə tiv)

(*adj.*) tending to produce a strong feeling or response; arousing desire or appetite; irritating, annoying

The ideas presented in the film were so _____ that I thought about them for days.

SYNONYMS: stimulating, arousing, vexing, galling
ANTONYMS: dull, insipid, bland, unstimulating

18. recondite
(rek' ən dīt)

(*adj.*) exceeding ordinary knowledge and understanding

The theories of relativity can seem _____, even for people who are well versed in the sciences.

SYNONYMS: arcane, abstruse; ANTONYMS: simple, uncomplicated

19. reprobate
(rep' rə bāt)

(*n.*) a depraved, vicious, or unprincipled person, scoundrel; (*adj.*) corrupt or unprincipled; (*v.*) to disapprove of, condemn

_____ are usually more charming, funny, or thrilling in fiction than they are in life.

SYNONYMS: (*n.*) scoundrel, blackguard; (*adj.*) immoral, corrupt
ANTONYMS: (*n.*) saint; (*adj.*) upright, virtuous, moral

20. sedentary
(sed' ən ter ē)

(*adj.*) characterized by or calling for continued sitting; remaining in one place

She exchanged her _____ job for a position as a swimming instructor.

SYNONYMS: static, stationary; ANTONYMS: active, peripatetic

Choosing the Right Word

Select the **boldface** word that better completes each sentence. You might refer to the selection on pages 126–127 to see how most of these words are used in context.

1. The scholars who compiled the notes and (**annotations, provocations**) for my portable edition of Chaucer did a superb job of clarifying obscure or puzzling words and passages.

2. It was quite (**fortuitous, efficacious**) that we met the studio owner, since she was looking for a new artist to feature in her gallery.

3. The crass and (**reprobate, fortuitous**) conduct of those responsible for the scandal deserved public censure.

4. When my sister arrived at my tiny apartment with two very excited dogs, the place was thrown into absolute (**bedlam, annotation**).

Illustration of some of the pilgrims from Chaucer's *The Canterbury Tales*

5. My sad story is that after working in the yard for three hours in the hot sun cleaning up the yard, I received the (**imperious, munificent**) sum of $5.50.

6. Only a genius could have converted such a (**motley, gratuitous**) group of individuals, drawn from all walks of life, into a disciplined and efficient organization.

7. Instead of relying on facts and logic, she used all kinds of rhetorical tricks and slashing (**invective, equanimity**) to attack her opponent.

8. The proverb "Make haste slowly" endorses prudence—not (**invective, procrastination**).

9. Instead of that highly involved and (**recondite, debonair**) discussion of the nation's energy needs, why don't you simply tell us what we can do to help solve the problem?

10. The queen strode into the chamber and (**imperiously, munificently**) commanded her subjects to be silent.

11. After working for a year at the same job, I was hoping that I had (**dunned, accrued**) enough vacation days to take a week off and travel to California.

12. This new book is a(n) (**imperious, provocative**) examination of our school system that may upset some of your most cherished ideas about higher education.

13. It is generally agreed that we urgently need more (**efficacious, reprobate**) methods of handling criminals, both for their own benefit and for that of the public.

14. Research shows that those who lead a (**gratuitous, sedentary**) lifestyle are more prone to chronic medical conditions, such as heart disease and diabetes.

15. What good will it do you to (**dun, procrastinate**) me so mercilessly when you know that I am flat broke?

16. To bear evils with (**invective, equanimity**) doesn't mean that you should make no effort to correct them.

17. The difficult stage part called for an actor to gradually change during the course of the play from a morose introvert to a(n) (**debonair, efficacious**) charmer.

18. Although they claimed that their summary gave us the (**bedlam, gist**) of the resolution, the fact is that it omitted important details.

19. During the war, soldiers assigned to desk jobs were sometimes sarcastically called the "chairbound infantry" or the "(**sedentary, recondite**) commandos."

20. We appreciated the services he furnished (**gratuitously, debonairly**), but we soon came to see that it would have been cheaper to pay for a really professional job.

21. I am convinced that some substantial advantages will surely (**accrue, procrastinate**) to me if I complete my college education.

22. His tone of voice was so (**munificent, imperious**) that I wasn't sure if he was asking me for a loan or demanding payment of tribute.

23. Scientists believe that everything in nature occurs in accordance with invariable laws and that nothing is truly (**imperious, fortuitous**).

24. He tried to make it appear that he was speaking in a friendly spirit, but I detected the (**recondite, covert**) malice beneath his "harmless" remarks.

25. Why does Sam (**procrastinate, reprobate**) whenever he has to write an essay?

Synonyms

*Choose the word from this unit that is the same or most nearly the same in meaning as the **boldface** word or expression in the phrase. Write that word on the line. Use a dictionary if necessary.*

1. **pestering** her for overdue payments _____

2. added **commentary** to the text _____

3. a **miscreant** in her business methods _____

4. the **general picture** of his story _____

5. an **assorted** crew of teens _____

6. a film with **unnecessary** scenes of violence _____

7. an angry **diatribe** _____

8. another excuse to **postpone** the assignment _____

9. an explanation too **esoteric** to follow _____

10. a **suave** greeting from our host _____

Antonyms

*Choose the word from this unit that is most nearly opposite in meaning to the **boldface** word or expression in the phrase. Write that word on the line. Use a dictionary if necessary.*

1. the racehorse's **lustrous** coat

   _____

2. a **uniform** arrangement of pictures on the wall

   _____

3. desiring her fans' **admiration**

   _____

4. display of **uncouth** manners

   _____

5. looking for a **champion**

   _____

Completing the Sentence

From the words in this unit, choose the one that best completes each of the following sentences. Write the word in the space provided.

1. We have seen her accept victory with grace; now can she face defeat with
   _____?

2. My opponent's last speech was filled with such acrimonious language and bitter
   _____ that I walked out of the room without even trying to reply.

3. It will be helpful if you can state the _____ of his arguments in a few sentences.

4. Our meeting seemed at the time to be entirely _____, but I learned later that it was the result of a careful plan.

5. It is up to the courts to decide how far police authorities may go in making use of
   _____ means of surveillance to catch criminals.

6. The kinds of books I enjoy reading range from light and airy comedies to
   _____ studies of social and philosophical problems.

7. In view of the fact that I have been driving for many years without having a single accident, his advice on how to handle a car seemed entirely _____.

8. Anyone who _____ when the opportunity to make a very profitable deal presents itself is not going to be notably successful in the business world.

9. Think of the great advantages that will _____ for all of us if we can carry out a truly effective program to conserve and maintain our natural resources.

10. His elegant appearance was matched by the _____ ease and polish of his manners.

11. No sooner had the incorrigible old _____ gotten out of jail than he returned to the wicked ways that had landed him there in the first place.

12. Next day, the instructor returned my thesis with a number of comments, queries, and other _____ penciled in the margin.

13. As the British writer W. Somerset Maugham once observed, human nature is a(n) _____ collection of strengths and weaknesses, foibles and follies.

14. This research program is entirely devoted to developing a drug that will be _____ in the treatment of arthritis.

15. Daily exercise is recommended particularly for people whose occupations are, for the most part, _____.

16. She is a leader who can command loyalty and instant obedience without resorting to abusive language, threats, or a(n) _____ manner.

17. Although their language was deliberately _____, I did not allow it to cause me to lose my self-control.

18. If you resent being _____ by tradespeople, why not try paying your bills on time?

19. The _____ gift of the Mellon family made it possible to set up the National Gallery of Art in Washington, D.C.

20. _____ broke out in the meeting hall as the speaker tried vainly to be heard over the angry shouting of the audience.

Writing: Words in Action

1. Look back at "Sinking Nation" (pages 126–127). Suppose you are a Tuvaluan who wants to relocate with your fellow citizens. You all want to maintain your identity as a people and a culture. Write a persuasive letter to the United Nations, stating your case. Use at least two details from the passage and three unit words.

2. Think about what you have learned about climate change, in particular how climate change has begun to affect the way people live. Write an essay about the effects, both natural and human-caused, of climate change (pages 126–127). Support your essay with specific details, your observations and studies, and the reading. Write at least three paragraphs, and use three or more words from this unit.

Vocabulary in Context

Literary Text

The following excerpts are from Innocents Abroad *by Mark Twain. Some of the words you have studied in this unit appear in **boldface** type. Complete each statement below the excerpt by circling the letter of the correct answer.*

1. . . . I shall not tell of the **motley** multitudes and wild costumes that graced a fair we found in full blast at another barbarous station; I shall not tell how we feasted on fresh dates and enjoyed the pleasant landscape all through the flying journey. . . .

A **motley** crowd is one that is

a. tranquil   **c.** ridiculous
b. diverse   **d.** homogeneous

2. We wished to go to the Ambrosian Library, and we did that also. We saw a manuscript of Virgil, with **annotations** in the handwriting of Petrarch, the gentleman who loved another man's Laura, and lavished upon her all through life a love which was a clear waste of the raw material. It was sound sentiment, but bad judgment.

Annotations in a manuscript are

a. indices   **c.** comments
b. illustrations   **d.** lessons

3. There was a muleteer to every donkey and a dozen volunteers beside, and they banged the donkeys with their goad sticks, and pricked them with their spikes, and shouted something that sounded like *"Sekki-yah!"* and kept up a din and a racket that was worse than **Bedlam** itself.

Bedlam is a state of

a. turmoil   **c.** regret
b. serenity   **d.** preservation

4. ...I had used strong language after promising I would never do so again; but the **provocation** was more than human nature could bear.

A **provocation** is an

a. account   **c.** amusement
b. invention   **d.** annoyance

Mark Twain relaxing on a ship deck in 1901.

5. They traveled in many lands, and had many strange adventures. They were virtuous young men, and lost no opportunity that fell in their way to make their livelihood. Their motto was in these words, namely, "**Procrastination** is the thief of time."

Procrastination is NOT an act of

a. postponement   **c.** suspension
b. accomplishment   **d.** deferment

Interactive Quiz

Snap the code, or go to
vocabularyworkshop.com

*Read the following selection, taking note of the **boldface** words and their contexts. These words are among those you will be studying in Unit 11. As you complete the exercises in this unit, it may help to refer to the way the words are used below.*

Oyez! Oyez!: The Evolution of News

<Informational Essay>

It has long been said that bad news travels fast, but nowadays it might be said that all news travels fast. The ability of human societies to **disseminate** information over great distances has improved immensely over the centuries, spurred by the advance of technology.

In ancient times, people sent messages from a distance using drums, smoke, and fire as signals. While these techniques served a purpose, the range of information they delivered was limited, and most news spread by word of mouth. Communicating across distances was **contingent** on travel, and the speed of delivery was limited by the pace of the messenger. Ancient civilizations built networks of roads and relay stations to promote communication. Foot runners entrusted with delivering urgent official news were selected from among the strongest and most **abstemious** young men, who were

Persian messenger, fourteenth century

The Smoke Signal, by Frederic Remington

considered the most responsible. The Royal Road constructed by the Persian Empire stretched over 1,500 miles and had over 100 stations where riders exchanged their tired horses for fresh mounts. Riding day and night, Persian messengers could cross the Empire in seven days. Ancient communication also benefited from the invention of writing and related technologies, such as paper and papyrus. Town criers with loud voices, expressive gestures, and **florid** outfits provided news to town **denizens**. Their cries of "Oyez! Oyez!" (Hear ye! Hear ye!) notified listeners of news to follow.

During the European Renaissance, merchants circulated handwritten newsletters containing information about international trade and foreign customs. Printed news pamphlets, made possible by the invention of the printing press, were a **salient** part of the fifteenth century. The first real newspapers appeared in Western Europe in the seventeenth century. At the time, European governments sought to use the newspapers to **inculcate** their own policies, imposing harsh penalties on publishers of political or religious **heresies**. Popular resistance to censorship gradually achieved increased freedom of the press. By the late nineteenth century, newspapers had become familiar throughout the world. News bureaus sprang up in cities across the globe to facilitate the collection of news, benefiting from the invention of the electric telegraph and telephone. News became a big business, and journalism became an important profession. Many newspapers published "yellow journalism," **foisting** poorly researched stories, **specious** rhetoric, and sensational scandals on their readers. To correct these **censurable** practices, a new breed of journalists, led by Joseph Pulitzer, attempted to impose professional standards in the industry. They emphasized unbiased reporting, research, and fact-checking to **corroborate** information.

The newspaper industry began to decline during the twentieth century as new technologies emerged. Newspaper circulation dropped as radio and television broadcast news directly into homes, providing instantaneous reports on the latest events. Since the 1990s, the Internet has become an increasingly important source of news. Thousands of Web sites offer news today, ranging from official government sites, to professional news organizations, to aimless, **discursive** blogs. Internet access, social media, and mobile devices enable people all over the world to capture photographs and video of events and publish them online for a global audience.

An electronic tablet, 2010

Some critics claim that the internet has **pernicious** effects on the news industry, eroding standards of journalism and spreading rumors and opinions instead of facts. Others applaud the Internet's contribution to the industry and to democratic debate. While the argument rages on, **perceptive** audiences learn to tell fact from fiction, and the steady churn of technology prepares the way for the future course of the evolution of the news.

Printing press, circa 1960

iWords

Snap the code, or go to **vocabularyworkshop.com**

Definitions

Note the spelling, pronunciation, part(s) of speech, and definition(s) of each of the following words. Then write the word in the blank spaces in the illustrative sentence(s) following. Finally, study the lists of synonyms and antonyms.

1. **abstemious**
(ab stē′ mē əs)

(*adj.*) moderate, sparing (as in eating and drinking); characterized by abstinence and self-discipline

She came from a long line of quiet, thrifty, and

_____ farming folk.

SYNONYMS: temperate, sober, moderate
ANTONYMS: indulgent, immoderate, intemperate

2. **censurable**
(sen′ shər ə bəl)

(*adj.*) deserving of blame or correction

Because he was unaware of what he had done, we decided that his behavior was not _____.

SYNONYMS: blameworthy, discreditable, reprehensible
ANTONYMS: commendable, laudable, meritorious

3. **contingent**
(kən tin′ jənt)

(*adj.*) likely but not certain to happen, possible; dependent on uncertain events or conditions; happening by chance; (*n.*) a representative group forming part of a larger body

_____ on our parents' approval, we plan to take a trip through Alaska next summer.

The meeting was delayed due to the late arrival of the California _____.

SYNONYMS: (*adj.*) conditional, dependent; (*n.*) a detachment
ANTONYMS: (*adj.*) independent of, unconnected with, certain

4. **corroborate**
(kə räb′ ə rāt)

(*v.*) to confirm, make more certain, bolster, substantiate, verify

He could tell the court where I was and for how long, but he needed a witness to _____ his statements.

ANTONYMS: (*adj.*) refute, contradict, undermine, discredit

5. **denizen**
(den′ ə zən)

(*n.*) an inhabitant, resident; one who frequents a place

A lover of marine life, she knew the names of all the scaly _____ of our lake.

SYNONYMS: dweller, habitué; ANTONYMS: alien, outsider, foreigner

6. **discursive**
(dis kər′ siv)

(*adj.*) passing aimlessly from one place or subject to another, rambling, roving, nomadic

Within the _____ account of his life, there was a fairly complete history of the whole village.

SYNONYMS: diffuse, wandering, episodic
ANTONYMS: short and to the point, succinct

7. disseminate
(di sem' ə nāt)

(v.) to scatter or spread widely

I decided that it was a bad idea to use my position in order to _____ my personal views.

SYNONYMS: disperse, publicize, broadcast, circulate
ANTONYMS: bring together, concentrate, muster, conceal, hide

8. dowdy
(daủ' dē)

(adj.) poorly dressed, shabby; lacking smartness and good taste

The actor wore _____ clothing and sunglasses so that no one would recognize him.

SYNONYMS: frumpy, frowsy; ANTONYMS: chic, elegant, fashionable

9. florid
(flär' id)

(adj.) highly colored, reddish; excessively ornate, showy

The _____ style of architecture in the old part of town was a welcome change from the grim, newer blocks we had seen.

SYNONYMS: flushed, ruddy, frilly, flamboyant
ANTONYMS: pale, ashen, pallid, sallow, austere, stark

10. foist
(foist)

(v.) to impose by fraud; to pass off as worthy or genuine; to bring about by stealth, dishonesty, or coercion

During the nineteenth century the unscrupulous Jay Gould _____ thousands of worthless railroad shares on an unsuspecting public.

SYNONYMS: pass off, palm off, fob off

11. gauche
(gōsh)

(adj.) awkward, lacking in social graces, tactless, clumsy

Though he was sincere when he thanked his guest for having stayed an extra week, his comment was considered

_____.

SYNONYMS: inept, uncouth, maladroit
ANTONYMS: adroit, tactful, diplomatic, politic

12. heresy
(her' ə sē)

(n.) an opinion different from accepted belief; the denial of an idea that is generally held sacred

Saving money to accumulate interest seems to be a form of _____ in these days of instant credit.

SYNONYMS: unorthodox belief, heterodoxy; ANTONYM: orthodoxy

13. inculcate
(in' kəl kāt)

(v.) to impress on the mind by repetition, teach persistently and earnestly

It is important to _____ a healthy respect for authority into army recruits.

SYNONYMS: instill, implant, infuse, ingrain, imbue
ANTONYMS: efface, extirpate, root out

14. **palpable**
(pal′ pə bəl)

(*adj.*) capable of being touched or felt; easily seen, heard, or recognized

The energy and excitement in the stands was almost _____ during the football game.

SYNONYMS: obvious, manifest; ANTONYMS: intangible, insubstantial

15. **perceptive**
(pər sep′ tiv)

(*adj.*) having sympathetic insight or understanding, capable of keen appreciation

His _____ eye took in the roomful of noisy children and settled on the one child who was ill at ease.

SYNONYMS: insightful, discerning; ANTONYMS: dense, obtuse

16. **pernicious**
(per nish′ əs)

(*adj.*) extremely harmful; deadly, fatal

Night air was once thought to have a _____ effect on infants who were in poor health.

SYNONYMS: injurious, deleterious, baleful, noxious
ANTONYMS: harmless, innocuous, salutary, salubrious

17. **salient**
(sāl′ yənt)

(*adj.*) leaping, jumping, or springing forth; prominent, standing out, conspicuous; (*n.*) a projection or bulge, a land form that projects upward or outward

I think the most _____ feature of the new plan is its similarity to the old plan.

Our forces occupied a _____ that was extremely vulnerable to attack.

SYNONYMS: (*adj.*) striking, notable, protrusive, obvious
ANTONYMS: (*adj.*) inconspicuous, recessive

18. **satiate**
(*v.*, sā′ shē āt;
adj., sā′ shē it)

(*v.*) to satisfy completely; to fill to excess; (*adj.*) full, satisfied

Nothing will _____ my hunger.

The _____ brown bear had a good sleep after raiding the honey-laden beehives.

SYNONYMS: (*v.*) surfeit, gorge; ANTONYM: (*v.*) deprive entirely of

19. **sear**
(sir)

(*v.*) to make or become dry and withered; to char or scorch the surface of; to harden or make unfeeling; to parch, singe

We wanted to serve grilled vegetables, but I _____ them, and they tasted like leather.

20. **specious**
(spē′ shəs)

(*adj.*) deceptive, apparently good or valid but lacking real merit

Though her résumé looked very impressive, her claims of vast experience in the field were _____.

SYNONYMS: deceptively plausible, sophistic, casuistic
ANTONYMS: valid, sound, solid, genuine

Choosing the Right Word

*Select the **boldface** word that better completes each sentence. You might refer to the selection on pages 136–137 to see how most of these words are used in context.*

1. As the Scottish poet Robert Burns aptly suggests, even the best-laid plans are often entirely (**palpable, contingent**) on events we cannot control.

2. Disguised as an old hag, the wicked queen gave Snow White a (**florid, pernicious**) apple, which trapped the young heroine into a prolonged, death-like sleep.

3. Before we (**inculcate, foist**) certain principles in young people, let's be sure that these principles are truly desirable for them and their society.

4. During times of extreme economic hardship and war, families often eat (**dowdily, abstemiously**).

5. Children are often remarkably (**discursive, perceptive**) in understanding how adults feel about them.

Illustration for the Brothers Grimm fairy tale, "Snow White"

6. With the advent of the Internet and e-mail, it is easy to (**disseminate, inculcate**) false information and rumors rapidly.

7. Although the essays are highly (**discursive, dowdy**), covering a wide range of topics, they are written with such clarity and grace that they are easy to follow.

8. In a series of (**searing, contingent**) attacks now known as the *Philippics,* Cicero launched his entire battery of political invective against the hapless Mark Anthony.

9. We are most likely to fall victim to (**discursive, specious**) reasoning when we have an emotional desire to believe what we are being told.

10. The article described the success of an undercover sting operation in catching the swindler who was (**foisting, searing**) fake diamonds on his customers.

11. The most tragic aspect of a forest fire is its destructive effects on the innumerable plant and animal (**heresies, denizens**) of that environment.

12. He thought he was being witty and charming, but I regard his conduct at the party as altogether (**abstemious, gauche**).

13. Modern nutritionists emphasize that there is a(n) (**palpable, abstemious**) difference between "eating to live" and "living to eat."

14. The more we studied the drug problem, the more we became aware of its (**contingent, pernicious**) influence on the American people today.

15. The study of history teaches us that many ideas regarded as (**heresies, disseminations**) by one generation are accepted as sound and orthodox by the next.

16. Some English rulers were strikingly elegant and imposing figures; others were somewhat (**specious, dowdy**) and unprepossessing.

17. No doubt his efforts to advance his own interests were (**censurable, florid**), but let's try to keep a sense of proportion and not condemn him too much.

18. Her (**perceptive, florid**) writing style, abounding in adjectives and fancy metaphors, is far from suitable for factual newspaper stories.

19. She was so (**abstemious, palpable**) that she extended her self-control even to her beloved books, and read them no more than an hour each day.

20. All the available evidence (**corroborates, foists**) my theory that the theft was planned by someone familiar with the layout of the house.

21. Although the Declaration of Independence was framed only to justify a revolution in the British colonies in North America, its ideas and ideals have been (**disseminated, seared**) throughout the world.

22. Don't you get tired of glossy advertisements that try to (**foist, satiate**) short-lived and sometimes absurd fashion trends on the consumer?

23. Out of all the endless flow of dull verbiage in that long lecture, we could recognize only two or three (**gauche, salient**) points.

24. Though I rather like the better TV game shows, I find that after a certain point, I'm (**satiated, inculcated**) and ready for more substantial fare.

25. A passing grade is (**pernicious, contingent**) on your participation in class.

Synonyms

*Choose the word from this unit that is the same or most nearly the same in meaning as the **boldface** word or expression in the phrase. Write that word on the line. Use a dictionary if necessary.*

1. a long and **digressive** novel _____

2. **tacky** window decorations _____

3. not tolerating **vulgar** behavior _____

4. take care not to **burn** the food _____

5. **authenticate** a silly rumor _____

6. a **flowery** introduction _____

7. a **tangible** change in the mood of the crowd _____

8. their **discriminating** remarks _____

9. **gratify** the appetite for gossip _____

10. a **native** of the high country _____

Antonyms

*Choose the word from this unit that is most nearly opposite in meaning to the **boldface** word or expression in the phrase. Write that word on the line. Use a dictionary if necessary.*

1. an **elusive** dream _____

2. an **unfulfilled** ambition _____

3. wearing **stylish** clothes _____

4. serve a **moist** turkey _____

5. a few **refined** guests _____

Completing the Sentence

From the words in this unit, choose the one that best completes each of the following sentences. Write the word in the space provided.

1. Unless you can produce witnesses to _____ your claim that you stopped at the red light, the mere assertion will have little or no effect on the jury.

2. The stubborn refusal to give me a chance to compete for the scholarship on the same basis as everyone else is a(n) _____ injustice to the whole idea of fair play.

3. I don't like to criticize your behavior, but I feel obliged to tell you that your discourtesy to that confused tourist was highly _____.

4. Is there any need for me to describe at length the _____ effects of smoking?

5. A(n) _____ characteristic of every great athlete is the ability to perform at maximum efficiency under extreme pressure.

6. The old fellow did indeed look like a typical _____ of the racetrack, as described in Damon Runyon's famous stories.

7. Though this may not be the most stylish blouse I own, I thought to myself, at least it doesn't make me look _____!

8. No honest mechanic will try to _____ inferior replacement parts on his customers.

9. If you wish to seal in the juices and bring out the flavor of your pot roast, _____ it briefly in a hot pan before you put it in the oven.

10. His talk on world affairs was so unorganized and _____ that it left us more confused than ever.

11. If I had the time, I could point out many flaws in the _____ arguments you find so impressive.

12. Since we wished to have some say in the town council's final decision, we sent a small _____ of our most persuasive speakers to the hearings.

13. The purpose of this program is to _____ throughout the community information about job-training opportunities for young people.

14. Eudora Welty is considered one of the most _____ and insightful American writers of her time.

15. When I referred to her favorite singer as an "untalented, overpaid, and conceited lout," she looked at me in shock, as though I had been guilty of _____.

16. It is hard to believe that people coming from such a refined social milieu could actually be so _____ and boorish.

17. After the long summer vacation, I was _____ with loafing and eager to return to school!

18. Psychologists tell us that the years of early childhood are the best time to _____ basic concepts of right and wrong.

19. Among all those pale and sallow people, her highly _____ complexion stood out like a beacon.

20. Her good health in old age is due in large part to the _____ habits of her younger years.

Writing: Words in Action

1. Look back at "Oyez! Oyez!: The Evolution of News" (pages 136–137). Suppose you are a reporter for a local newspaper. The newspaper's owners have decided to cancel print media and post all news online, with a focus on national and world news. Write a letter persuading the owners that local news is important and that there should be both print and online versions of the newspaper. Use at least two details from the passage and three unit words.

2. Write an essay in which you analyze how the proliferation of news sources such as the Internet, 24-hour cable news TV stations, and satellite radio has affected modern life. Has the availability of "instant news" changed our lives for the better, or has it had negative effects? Support your essay with specific details, your observations and studies, and the reading (pages 136–137). Write at least three paragraphs, and use three or more words from this unit.

Vocabulary in Context

Literary Text

The following excerpts are from The Beautiful and Damned *by F. Scott Fitzgerald. Some of the words you have studied in this unit appear in* **boldface** *type. Complete each statement below the excerpt by circling the letter of the correct answer.*

1. Outside the world of the company there appeared, from time to time, the colonel, a heavy man with snarling teeth, who circumnavigated the battalion drill-field upon a handsome black horse. He was a West Pointer, and, mimetically, a gentleman. He had a **dowdy** wife and a **dowdy** mind, and spent much of his time in town taking advantage of the army's lately exalted social position.

   Someone who is **dowdy** is NOT
   a. boring   c. dull
   b. shabby   d. stylish

2. She was almost painfully refined—she wore a last year's hat covered with violets no more yearningly pretentious and **palpably** artificial than herself.

   A **palpably** artificial adornment is one whose artificiality is
   a. obvious   c. ostentatious
   b. valuable   d. inconspicuous

3. He remembered the Gloria who promised that should she ever want anything, she would take it...it was only the effect on a person's mind that counted, anyhow, she said, and her reaction would be the masculine one, of **satiation** and faint dislike.

   A state of **satiation** is one of
   a. depravity   c. complete gratification
   b. apprehension   d. reserved acceptance

F. Scott Fitzgerald, chronicler of the Jazz Age, with his wife Zelda

4. They decided that for the present she was not to go with him to the Southern camp where his **contingent** was ordered. She would remain in New York to "use the apartment," to save money, and to watch the progress of the case....

   A **contingent** is a(n)
   a. embargo   c. tradition
   b. troop   d. business

5. "I wanted to see you—" began Anthony uncertainly. He did not feel that he could ask for a loan with the girl not four feet away, so he broke off and made a **perceptible** motion of his head as if to beckon Maury to one side.

   If a motion is **perceptible**, it is
   a. imposing   c. sneaky
   b. ambiguous   d. noticeable

Interactive Quiz

Snap the code, or go to
vocabularyworkshop.com

*Read the following selection, taking note of the **boldface** words and their contexts. These words are among those you will be studying in Unit 12. As you complete the exercises in this unit, it may help to refer to the way the words are used below.*

The Facts in the Case of the Greatest Mystery Writer

<Debate>

After his class read two Edgar Allan Poe stories, "The Murders in the Rue Morgue" (1841) and "The Purloined Letter" (1844), Mr. Shippen asked: *While Edgar Allan Poe deserves credit for inventing the modern detective story, are his stories the best examples of the genre?* A lively discussion between two students followed.

Nate: Poe's brilliant detective stories are rightly praised as **scintillating** forerunners of this genre in fiction. Poe's sharp, **incisive** style and his ability to establish and then **enhance** suspense fully justify his reputation as the master of the modern detective story. "The Murders in the Rue Morgue" and "The Purloined Letter" exhibit features that became standard in later detective fiction: A crime is committed, an investigation ensues, and an unexpected solution is discovered by the brilliant mental gymnastics of the detective.

Kyra: I strongly disagree with Nate's appraisal of Poe's detective stories. Let's begin with Poe's style. It is difficult to **absolve** Poe of the offenses of pomposity and digression. The opening of "The Murders in the Rue Morgue" consists of lengthy, abstract discussions of the concept of "analysis," and Poe's efforts to distinguish between analysis and ingenuity are **deleterious** to storytelling. Moreover, his style is more **prosaic** than evocative, more **redundant** than concise. Take the story's first sentence: "The mental features discoursed of as the analytical, are, in themselves, but little susceptible of analysis." Spare us, Edgar!

Nate: In detective stories, the character of the detective is paramount, and Poe invented a figure who became a **paragon** for the genre: the brilliant but idiosyncratic C. Auguste Dupin—the ancestor of Sherlock Holmes, Hercule Poirot, Miss Marple, and other fictional detectives. His powers of observation and deduction **enthrall** the reader, while he is seldom arrogant or **ostentatious**, except when he dryly mocks the limitations of the Paris police—thus establishing another common character in detectives stories, the inept local policeman.

Illustration from "The Raven," 1864

Above: Basil Rathbone and Nigel Bruce in "Sherlock Holmes Faces Death," 1943

Kyra: Dupin is not nearly as impressive as Conan Doyle's Sherlock Holmes. In the "Rue Morgue," Poe violates what many readers would regard as a compact between author and reader by making the murderer an escaped orangutan! Dupin releases the animal's owner of any responsibility—an action with which many readers disagree.

Nate: Look before you leap, Kyra! Since you referred to Sherlock Holmes, it's worth observing that in his detective tales, Poe establishes a first-person narrator who is the detective's close personal friend. Conan Doyle followed exactly this pattern with Sherlock Holmes and Dr. Watson, and Conan Doyle himself credits Poe as his inspiration.

As for the story's plot in "Rue Morgue," a central part of the puzzle is a **clangor** of shrieks and cries heard by witnesses. From the evidence, Dupin discerns an **implicit** conclusion: one participant in the crime was a human, while the other was not. This conclusion is supported by the issue of motive, and the fact that a large amount of money was left untouched suggests that the murders were not the result of **cupidity**. In "The Purloined Letter," furthermore, Dupin shows himself to be a master of **politic** behavior as he subtly disarms a powerful government minister who has resorted to blackmail.

Kyra: I'm sorry, Nate, but "The Purloined Letter" does little to **extenuate** Poe's clumsiness in this genre. The two-dimensional dialogue often descends to **caricature**, and the plot depends on a twofold substitution of a duplicate for the stolen letter. Such repetition is awkward and **inimical** to credibility. However **winsome** Dupin may be, I don't believe that the detective could have tricked the villain with the same device that the blackmailer himself employed to obtain the letter in the first place.

Mr. Shippen: We will have to agree to disagree, as the class period ended five minutes ago!

Snap the code, or go to
vocabularyworkshop.com

Definitions

Note the spelling, pronunciation, part(s) of speech, and definition(s) of each of the following words. Then write the word in the blank spaces in the illustrative sentence(s) following. Finally, study the lists of synonyms and antonyms.

1. absolve
(ab zälv´)

(v.) to clear from blame, responsibility, or guilt

They assumed that their alibi would _____ them of suspicion.

SYNONYMS: acquit, exonerate, vindicate, excuse, pardon
ANTONYMS: condemn, convict, incriminate, inculpate

2. caricature
(kar´ i kə chür)

(n.) a representation, such as a drawing, that exaggerates a subject's characteristic features; (v.) to present someone or something in a deliberately distorted way

What began as a hasty newspaper _____ soon turned up on coffee mugs, T-shirts, and sweatshirts.

The satirical television program _____ the movie star and made him seem clumsier than he really was.

SYNONYMS: (n.) cartoon, burlesque, lampoon

3. clangor
(klang´ ər)

(n.) a loud ringing sound; (v.) to make a loud ringing noise

For more than a century, American grade schools summoned children to school with the _____ of a bell.

SYNONYMS: (n.) din, clamor, uproar
ANTONYMS: (n.) silence, stillness, peace and quiet

4. contiguous
(kən tig´ yü əs)

(adj.) side by side, touching; near; adjacent in time

Trouble arose over who should control the weeds and bushes that rioted in the lot _____ to ours.

SYNONYMS: abutting, next door to
ANTONYMS: detached, apart, distant, remote

5. cupidity
(kyü pid´ ə tē)

(n.) an eager desire for something; greed

You say that these catalogue prices show the quality of the goods, but I say they show the seller's

_____.

SYNONYMS: avarice, rapacity, craving, lust
ANTONYMS: contentment, satiety, gratification

6. deleterious
(del ə tir´ ē əs)

(adj.) harmful, injurious

Wishing can give zest and purpose to anyone's life, but wishful thinking can have a _____ effect.

SYNONYMS: detrimental, destructive, pernicious, damaging
ANTONYMS: helpful, beneficial, harmless, innocuous

7. enhance
(en hans')

(*v.*) to raise to a higher degree; to increase the value or desirability of

She sanded and varnished the old table in order to _____ its appearance and value.

SYNONYMS: improve, elevate; ANTONYMS: diminish, degrade

8. enthrall
(en thrôl')

(*v.*) to captivate, charm, hold spellbound; to enslave; to imprison

All the critics were _____ by the performance and wrote rave reviews.

SYNONYMS: fascinate, attract; ANTONYMS: bore to tears, repel

9. extenuate
(ek sten' yü āt)

(*v.*) to lessen the seriousness or magnitude of an offense by making partial excuses

"Do not _____ the circumstances!" my mom said when I explained I had been studying rather than cleaning my room.

SYNONYMS: moderate, mitigate, diminish, downplay
ANTONYMS: intensify, magnified, worsen, exacerbate

10. implicit
(im plis' it)

(*adj.*) implied or understood though unexpressed; without doubts or reservations, unquestioning; potentially contained in

She never said so, but it was _____ that she did not like conversations before her morning coffee.

SYNONYMS: inferred, tacit, unspoken, unconditional
ANTONYMS: explicit, expressed, stated, revealed

11. incisive
(in sī' siv)

(*adj.*) sharp, keen, penetrating (with a suggestion of decisiveness and effectiveness)

I am truly thankful for your _____ remarks about my report.

SYNONYMS: acute, cutting, perceptive

12. inimical
(in im'i kəl)

(*adj.*) tending to cause harm or obstruct developments; being oppositional or adverse

Several _____ groups have tried to create chaos and undermine democratic principles.

SYNONYMS: unfriendly, hostile, antagonistic, contrary
ANTONYMS: friendly, hospitable, kind

13. ostentatious
(äs ten tā' shəs)

(*adj.*) marked by conspicuous or pretentious display, showy

The restaurant's interior was so _____ that the meager meal, when it came, seemed an afterthought.

SYNONYMS: flashy, overdone, affected, flamboyant
ANTONYMS: modest, plain, simple, demure, retiring

14. paragon
(par′ ə gän)

(*n.*) a model of excellence or perfection

I may not be a _____ of scholarship, but I do try my best.

SYNONYMS: ideal, paradigm, model, good example

15. politic
(päl′ ə tik)

(*adj.*) prudent, shrewdly conceived and developed; artful, expedient

In your angry state I think it would be _____ to say nothing, at least until you have calmed down.

SYNONYMS: tactful, diplomatic, judicious, circumspect
ANTONYMS: unwise, injudicious, imprudent, rash

16. prosaic
(prō zā′ ik)

(*adj.*) dull, lacking in distinction and originality; matter-of-fact, straightforward; characteristic of prose, not poetic

I remember his singing voice as being on key and clear but also _____.

SYNONYMS: literal, pedestrian; ANTONYMS: remarkable, poetic

17. redundant
(ri dən′ dənt)

(*adj.*) extra, excess, more than is needed; wordy, repetitive; profuse, lush

Some _____ expressions, such as "hollow tubing," are acceptable in the English language.

SYNONYMS: unnecessary, superfluous, verbose, prolix
ANTONYMS: terse, laconic, scarce, inadequate

18. sanctimonious
(saŋk tə mō′ nē əs)

(*adj.*) making a show of virtue or righteousness; hypocritically moralistic or pious, self-righteous, canting, holier-than-thou

Cautionary tales that take on a _____ tone often achieve the opposite of the desired result.

ANTONYMS: heartfelt, sincere, humble

19. scintillating
(sin′ tə lāt iŋ)

(*adj., part.*) sparkling, twinkling, exceptionally brilliant (applied to mental or personal qualities)

She was known for her _____ conversation.

SYNONYMS: stimulating, glittering; ANTONYMS: dull, boring, insipid

20. winsome
(win′ səm)

(*adj.*) charming, attractive, pleasing (often suggesting a childlike charm and innocence)

When my little brother wanted something badly, he became as _____ as a puppy.

SYNONYMS: winning, delightful, prepossessing
ANTONYMS: unattractive, unappealing, repulsive

Choosing the Right Word

*Select the **boldface** word that better completes each sentence. You might refer to the selection on pages 146–147 to see how most of these words are used in context.*

1. In the Lincoln-Douglas debates, Lincoln asked a few (**incisive, prosaic**) questions that showed up the fatal weaknesses in his opponent's position.

2. The commander expected (**ostentatious, implicit**) obedience from his troops.

3. Rumors of "easy money" and "lush profits" to be made in the stock market aroused the (**clangor, cupidity**) of many small investors.

4. The proposed advertisement was supposed to be "dynamic" and a "real eye-catcher," but I found it utterly (**politic, prosaic**).

5. My five-year-old nephew enjoys telling (**inimical, ostentatious**) stories about his travels to strange lands in a giant balloon.

In 1858, Abraham Lincoln lost the Illinois Senate race to Stephen Douglas, who in turn lost his bid for the Presidency when Lincoln ran against him in 1860.

6. Broccoli, considered by dietitians to be a (**cupidity, paragon**) among vegetables, is packed with calcium and antioxidant properties.

7. As long as we are (**enthralled, extenuated**) by the idea that it is possible to get something for nothing, we will not be able to come up with a sound economic program.

8. The severe drought and locust infestation proved to have a (**deleterious, ostentatious**) effect on the harvest.

9. What we do now to remedy the evils in our society will determine whether or not we are to be (**absolved, enthralled**) of blame for the injustices of the past.

10. When he demanded that I immediately "return back" the money I owed him, I found him not merely unpleasant but (**redundant, winsome**).

11. I will try to tell the story in a balanced way, without either exaggerating or (**scintillating, extenuating**) his responsibility for those sad events.

12. Words about "tolerance" are empty and (**sanctimonious, contiguous**) when they come from one who has shown no concern about civil liberties.

13. The aspiring salesperson stood in front of the mirror for hours, practicing a (**winsome, prosaic**) smile.

14. I've heard that if you sprinkle cinnamon in coffee, it (**enthralls, enhances**) the flavor and diminishes the bitterness.

15. She delivered her lines with such artistry and verve that she made the rather commonplace dialogue seem (**scintillating, deleterious**).

16. "In seeking to discredit me," I replied, "my opponent has deliberately (**absolved, caricatured**) my ideas, making them seem simplistic and unrealistic."

17. We thought it best to buy a house that was close to my parents' home, but not (**prosaic, contiguous**) to it.

18. My parents set up my older brother as such a (**caricature, paragon**) that I despaired of ever being able to follow in his footsteps.

19. Isn't it rather (**ostentatious, redundant**) to wear a Phi Beta Kappa key on a chain around your neck?

20. A fresh coat of paint and some attention to the lawn would greatly (**enhance, absolve**) the appearance of our bungalow.

21. Isn't it logical to conclude that because poor eating habits have a (**prosaic, deleterious**) effect on one's health, you should not make snack foods the cornerstone of your diet?

22. It is hardly (**politic, clangorous**) for someone who hopes to win a popularity contest to go about making such brutally frank remarks.

23. I realized I was being kept awake not by the (**paragon, clangor**) of the city traffic but by a gnawing fear that I had done the wrong thing.

24. Any conduct that is (**inimical, sanctimonious**) to school policy, including violation of state laws, is grounds for immediate dismissal.

25. Our astute professor gave an (**incisive, implicit**) lecture on literary symbolism.

Synonyms

*Choose the word from this unit that is the same or most nearly the same in meaning as the **boldface** word or expression in the phrase. Write that word on the line. Use a dictionary if necessary.*

1. bought lots that were **adjoining**   _____

2. to **intensify** the taste of the sauce   _____

3. an **exemplar** of team spirit   _____

4. a **trenchant** report   _____

5. a **lively** play of wit   _____

6. the **commonplace** routines of housework   _____

7. a **parody** of his behavior   _____

8. a book with the power to **enchant**   _____

9. a **smug** accusation   _____

10. an **engaging** smile   _____

Antonyms

*Choose the word from this unit that is most nearly opposite in meaning to the **boldface** word or expression in the phrase. Write that word on the line. Use a dictionary if necessary.*

1. a person filled with **generosity**   _____

2. a **self-effacing** character   _____

3. charges **aggravated** by circumstances   _____

4. issuing **succinct** instructions   _____

5. battling **isolated** forest fires   _____

Completing the Sentence

From the words in this unit, choose the one that best completes each of the following sentences. Write the word in the space provided.

1. How can anyone be so foolish as to develop a smoking habit when it has been proven that cigarettes are _____ to health?

2. The fact that he had hungry children at home does not justify what he did, but it does _____ his crime.

3. In most contracts, there are _____ duties and obligations that must be fulfilled even though they aren't expressed in so many words.

4. The _____ of the fire bells as they echoed through the night filled our hearts with terror.

5. Because the gym is _____ to the library, it is easy for me to shift from academic to athletic activities.

6. Because we had been told the new TV series was original and witty, we were disappointed by the obvious and _____ situation comedy that unfolded on our screen.

7. Her new hairstyle greatly _____ her appearance.

8. Until he rose to speak, the meeting had been dull, but he immediately enlivened it with his _____ wit.

9. The jury may have found him not guilty, but the "court of public opinion" will never _____ him of responsibility for the crime.

10. We resented his _____ self-assurance that he was morally superior to everyone else.

11. Detective stories seem to _____ her to such a degree that she reads virtually nothing else.

12. She did her work so quietly that it took us time to realize that she was a veritable _____ of efficiency and diligence.

13. Though ranking officials on both sides hoped to reach a truce and prepare a peace treaty, fringe groups refused to suspend their _____ activities.

14. His long nose and prominent teeth give the candidate the kind of face that cartoonists love to _____.

15. There are some situations in life when it is _____ to remain quiet and wait for a better opportunity to assert yourself.

16. Marie's appealing personality and endearing manner make her quite _____ and engaging.

17. With that one _____ comment, she brought an end to all the aimless talk and directed our attention to the real problem facing us.

18. Over the years, his normal desire for financial security was gradually distorted into a boundless _____.

19. "Evening dress is far too _____ for such an informal occasion," I thought to myself as I tried to decide what to wear that night.

20. To characterize the literary style of Edgar Allan Poe as "unique and one of a kind" is certainly _____.

Writing: Words in Action

1. Look back at "The Facts in the Case of the Greatest Mystery Writer" (pages 146–147). Suppose you are one of Mr. Shippen's students. You have to persuade the class who the better mystery writer is—Poe or Doyle. Write an argument in favor of one writer, using at least two details from the passage and three unit words.

2. The term *mystery* is used to describe both a genre of fiction writing and elements of existence that are not fully understood. The search for answers to life's "mysteries" has led to countless achievements in science, mathematics, and the arts. In a brief essay, describe some ways in which the idea of "mystery" can inspire new discoveries or artistic creation. First, define your understanding of what a "mystery" is. Support your essay with specific details, your observations and studies, and the reading (pages 146–147). Write at least three paragraphs, and use three or more words from this unit.

Vocabulary in Context

The following excerpts are from **The Marble Faun** *by Nathaniel Hawthorne. Some of the words you have studied in this unit appear in* **boldface** *type. Complete each statement below the excerpt by circling the letter of the correct answer.*

1. The story of this adventure spread abroad, and made its way beyond the usual gossip of the Forestieri, even into Italian circles, where, **enhanced** by a still potent spirit of superstition, it grew far more wonderful than as above recounted.

Something that has been **enhanced** has been

a. improved **c.** expired
b. belittled **d.** weakened

2. "When women have other objects in life, they are not apt to fall in love. I can think of many women distinguished in art, literature, and science,— and multitudes whose hearts and minds find good employment in less **ostentatious** ways,— who lead high, lonely lives, and are conscious of no sacrifice so far as your sex is concerned."

If something is **ostentatious**, it is

a. unexceptional **c.** flamboyant
b. foolish **d.** frightening

3. . . . [H]is voice appeared to fill the air, yet not with an obtrusive **clangor**. The sound was of a murmurous character, soft, attractive, persuasive, friendly.

The Marble Faun is a murder mystery set in Rome, Italy.

A **clangor** is a(n)

a. pleasant tone **c.** angry announcement
b. loud noise **d.** simple gesture

4. "The disorder!" repeated Miriam. "There is none that I know of save too much life and strength, without a purpose for one or the other. It is my too **redundant** energy that is slowly—or perhaps rapidly—wearing me away, because I can apply it to no use. The object, which I am bound to consider my only one on earth, fails me utterly."

Energy that is **redundant** is NOT

a. sufficient **c.** abundant
b. renewable **d.** limited

5. Donatello had not very easily been stirred out of the peculiar sluggishness, which **enthralls** and bewitches melancholy people.

If something **enthralls** people it

a. enchants them **c.** saddens them
b. sickens them **d.** angers them

Interactive Quiz

Snap the code, or go to
vocabularyworkshop.com

Vocabulary for Comprehension

*Read the following selection in which some of the words you have studied in Units 10–12 appear in **boldface** type. Then answer the questions on page 157.*

This passage discusses early maps of the Americas, which were based on the memories of explorers and therefore full of errors.

(Line)

Modern maps record **palpable** scientific measurements, but in the Middle Ages maps drew upon the excited and imprecise recollections

(5) of hired explorers. Employed to aggrandize a nation's wealth by finding new colonies and better trade routes to the riches of India, these explorers were driven more

(10) by their clients' **cupidity** than by a thirst for scientific knowledge. Thus, they came to some **gratuitous** assumptions and made some big mistakes.

(15) Most commonly, explorers misjudged the size and shape of North and South America while searching the seas for Cathay. So intent was Columbus on reaching

(20) the East that he thought that Cuba, when he saw it, was actually Japan and that the coast of Central America was the shore of southern Asia. In 1525 Giovanni da Verrazano,

(25) sailing south of New England, "discovered" and named the "Sea of Verrazano," which cartographers dutifully included on their maps for the next hundred years. This grand

(30) waterway led, said Verrazano, to India and China; more likely it was the wet doorstep to North Carolina.

Eventually, rough sizes and shapes for North and South

(35) America—**caricatures**, really—were determined. But the ocean beyond them continued to be overlooked by European eyes fastened on Asia; for years the Pacific was mapped as a

(40) narrow strait between North America and Japan. Harder to explain is why California changed from being part of the mainland on some maps to an island on others.

(45) Juan Ponce de León, discovering Florida in 1513, reported that it, too, was an island (this was clearly not **corroborated** by the facts). But he didn't call it "land of flowers" (*flores*

(50) in Spanish), as some current **denizens** of the state might suppose. He found it on Easter, which the Spaniards called Pascua Florida for the flowers displayed in

(55) their churches. Ponce was honoring Easter.

Very old place names can also be confusing. North and South Carolina, once a single British colony, pay

(60) tribute to no one named Caroline. Instead, they honor King Charles I of England, who set up the colony and whose name in Latin was Carolus.

1. **Palpable** (line 1) most nearly means
   a. controversial
   b. questionable
   c. tangible
   d. accurate
   e. esoteric

2. The main idea of the first paragraph (lines 1–14) is that early explorers
   a. mastered the art of map-making
   b. knew all the trade routes to India
   c. were mainly motivated by scientific curiosity
   d. were not influenced by their clients
   e. made maps reflecting their erroneous assumptions

3. The meaning of **cupidity** (line 10) is
   a. affection
   b. avarice
   c. thrift
   d. stupidity
   e. repentance

4. **Gratuitous** (line 12) is best defined as
   a. unwarranted
   b. peculiar
   c. innovative
   d. predictable
   e. surprising

5. In paragraph 2 (lines 15–32), the author cites the examples of Columbus and Verrazano in order to show that
   a. Verrazano was influenced by Columbus's mistakes
   b. both were incompetent as explorers
   c. Columbus was an inspiring leader and Verrazano was not
   d. both misjudged the size and shape of the Americas
   e. each explorer's motivations were completely different

6. In lines 29–32, the contrast the writer draws results in
   a. symbolism
   b. anticlimax
   c. hyperbole
   d. restatement
   e. foreshadowing

7. According to paragraph 3 (lines 33–44), early maps of California
   a. misspelled its name
   b. exaggerated its size
   c. placed it in the center of North America
   d. attributed its discovery to Juan Ponce de León
   e. showed it sometimes as part of the mainland and sometimes as an island

8. **Caricatures** (line 35) are best defined as
   a. ringing endorsements
   b. loud noises
   c. distorted representations
   d. newspaper clippings
   e. hasty drawings

9. **Corroborated** (line 48) most nearly means
   a. substantiated
   b. reported
   c. contradicted
   d. described
   e. refuted

10. You can infer from paragraph 4 (lines 45–56) that which of the following played a role in the naming of Florida?
   a. trade
   b. religious customs
   c. geographic location
   d. the wishes of the King of Spain
   e. the appearance of the region's inhabitants

11. **Denizens** (line 51) is best defined as
   a. legislators
   b. employees
   c. inhabitants
   d. tourists
   e. critics

12. Which of the following best describes the writer's tone in the passage?
   a. nostalgic
   b. factual
   c. skeptical
   d. pessimistic
   e. admiring

Two-Word Completions

Select the pair of words that best complete the meaning of each of the following passages.

1. "The flamboyant plumage of the male of the species has always struck me as overly _____," the ornithologist observed. "In contrast, the female looks so drab and _____ in her somber browns and grays."
   a. debonair . . . censurable
   b. salient . . . gauche
   c. prosaic . . . scintillating
   d. ostentatious . . . dowdy

2. Office workers usually lead relatively _____ lives between nine and five. For that reason, many a "desk jockey" finds a weekly trip to the gym a(n) _____ way to keep fit.
   a. covert . . . gratuitous
   b. ostentatious . . . provocative
   c. sedentary . . . efficacious
   d. prosaic . . . pernicious

3. "We must take immediate steps to counteract this highly dangerous development," the new President told his advisors, "for the longer we _____, the more _____ its effects will be."
   a. procrastinate . . . pernicious
   b. corroborate . . . prosaic
   c. disseminate . . . deleterious
   d. accrue . . . inimical

4. Florida Fats and the other _____ of McDuffy's Billiard Emporium seem to come from every walk of life. One is unlikely to find such a(n) _____ crew under any other roof in town.
   a. denizens . . . motley
   b. caricatures . . . abstemious
   c. paragons . . . fortuitous
   d. reprobates . . . contiguous

5. Most of the adults seemed to find Kal's Kiddie Karnival a bit of a bore, but their children were _____, and the youngsters' appetites for the kind of fare that Kal served up were not _____ when the show was over.
   a. enhanced . . . accrued
   b. enthralled . . . satiated
   c. seared . . . absolved
   d. inculcated . . . extenuated

6. In a series of _____ attacks, chock-full of the most withering political _____, the famous orator Demosthenes fulminated against King Philip of Macedon's nefarious efforts to curtail Greek rights and liberties.
   a. scintillating . . . heresies
   b. gratuitous . . . clangor
   c. searing . . . invective
   d. motley . . . annotations

7. The whole purpose of _____ dozens of fliers, press releases, advertisements, and other media was to put a quick and sudden stop to the _____ rumors about our candidate, but the tales persisted.
   a. absolving . . . palpable
   b. procrastinating . . . provocative
   c. disseminating . . . pernicious
   d. accruing . . . gratuitous

Adages

In the essay "Oyez! Oyez!: The Evolution of News" (see pages 136–137), the author begins by citing an old saying, "Bad news travels fast." The saying means that people have a tendency to share negative stories more readily than they share good news.

"Bad news travels fast" is an **adage**, a short, clever saying that conveys observations and truths about human foibles and the nature of everyday experiences. Adages can be serious and admonishing or humorous and witty. These tidbits of folk wisdom, which have been passed down from generation to generation, have become integrated into our daily language.

Choosing the Right Adage

Read each sentence. Use context clues to figure out the meaning of each adage in **boldface** *print. Then write the letter of the definition for the adage in the sentence.*

1. Instead of spending your time worrying about what your brother is doing, just **live and let live**. _____

2. **Rats will always desert a sinking ship**, so it was no surprise that employees started to leave Lisa's company in droves when profits sank. _____

3. Before you spend your entire savings on that expensive new car, you should **sleep on it**. _____

4. The only way to meet the deadline for this huge project is to **divide and conquer**. _____

5. The parents kept texting from their phones during the entire restaurant meal in order to give their teenage children **a taste of their own medicine**. _____

6. After the waiter spilled a smoothie all over my new dress, there was nothing I could do except **grin and bear it**. _____

7. My father always believes my sister, but he forgets that **there are two sides to a coin**. _____

8. I did not tell Linda that her apple pie tasted horrible. **What she doesn't know won't hurt her**. _____

9. Before you spend money on cosmetic surgery, remember that **true beauty lies within**. _____

10. **Practice makes perfect**, so I think it's much too soon for you to give up your dream of becoming a professional musician. _____

a. Keeping unpleasant truths to yourself can spare a friend's feelings.

b. Tackle a big task by breaking it into more manageable pieces.

c. Think carefully before making a decision.

d. Calmly accept something you can't change.

e. Inner qualities are more important than outward appearances.

f. Repetition helps you learn something well.

g. People will leave when they know there are serious problems.

h. Teach others a lesson by acting as they do.

i. There is more than one side to every story.

j. Accept that other people have their own way of doing things.

Writing with Adages

Find the meaning of each adage. (Use an online or print dictionary if necessary.) Then write a sentence for each adage.

1. There's no such thing as a free lunch.

_____

2. Measure twice, cut once.

_____

3. What goes around, comes around.

_____

4. Looks can be deceiving.

_____

5. An eye for an eye leaves the whole world blind.

_____

_____

6. Laughter is the best medicine.

_____

_____

7. Can't never could.

_____

_____

8. Ignorance is bliss.

_____

9. Honesty is the best policy.

_____

10. It's time to pay the piper.

_____

11. Time to eat crow.

_____

12. Be careful what you wish for.

_____

Denotation and Connotation

The **denotation** of a word is its literal meaning, the one found in the dictionary. A denotation is neutral, free from any emotional associations. A **connotation** is the emotional association a reader makes to a word. A word can evoke positive or negative connotations.

Consider these synonyms for the neutral word *sear*:

> *grill   broil   burn   scorch*

For a chef, *grill* and *broil* are methods of preparing food; the words have neutral or even positive connotations. A chef would find the words *burn* and *scorch* to have very negative connotations, however—no cook wants to burn or scorch food.

> **Think:** A recipe might suggest that you grill or broil a piece of meat or fish, but no recipe ever suggests burning or scorching food!

Look at these examples of words that are similar in denotation but have different connotations.

NEUTRAL	POSITIVE	NEGATIVE
pleasant	debonair	slick
representation	cartoon	caricature
unadorned	simple	dowdy

Professional writers and speakers understand the importance of connotation. A political candidate carefully chooses words for speeches, knowing that connotations can sway voters' minds. A poet carefully crafts a poem, making sure that each word's connotation is appropriate for the tone and message of the work.

Shades of Meaning

Write a plus sign (+) in the box if the word has a positive connotation.
Write a minus sign (–) if the word has a negative connotation. Put a zero (0)
if the word is neutral.

1. reprobate ☐   **2.** gauche ☐   **3.** enhance ☐   **4.** bedlam ☐

5. clangor ☐   **6.** paragon ☐   **7.** absolve ☐   **8.** contiguous ☐

9. denizen ☐   **10.** perceptive ☐   **11.** gist ☐   **12.** foist ☐

13. sanctimonious ☐   **14.** censurable ☐   **15.** winsome ☐   **16.** inimical ☐

Expressing the Connotation

Read each sentence. Select the word in parentheses that expresses the connotation (positive, negative, or neutral) given at the beginning of the sentence.

neutral
1. Kelly is not one who likes to (**procrastinate, wait**) when she has a deadline to meet.

positive
2. The chief executive officer answered the shareholder's question with a (**politic, shrewd**) response.

negative
3. We did not want Sheila in our study group because of her (**tyrannical, imperious**) attitude toward others.

positive
4. Everyone at the concert hall was (**pleased, enthralled**) with the maestro's interpretation of Bach.

negative
5. The audience, appalled at the speaker's (**invective, criticism**), left the room in droves.

positive
6. To show his appreciation to those who taught him to read, Mr. Halstead made a (**generous, munificent**) donation to the school's library.

negative
7. Some snake bites have a (**deleterious, lethal**) effect on humans.

neutral
8. Though the scientist conducted (**incisive, cutting-edge**) research, no one believed the new drug would curtail the flu epidemic.

Challenge: Using Connotation

Choose vocabulary words from Units 10–12 to replace the highlighted words in the sentences below. Then explain how the connotation of the replacement word changes the tone of the sentence.

abstemious	**fortuitous**	**provocative**
sedentary	**gratuitous**	**debonair**

1. Missing our connection at the airport was **unplanned** _____; as it turned out, that flight experienced mechanical problems and had to be grounded.

_____

_____

2. After injuring her back, the doctor suggested that Ms. Stevenson limit herself to **idle** _____ activities.

_____

_____

3. Last night, we attended an avant-garde play in which the character's speeches were at once philosophical and **vexing** _____.

_____

_____

Classical Roots

equa, equi, ega, iqui—equal

This root appears in **equanimity** (page 129). The literal meaning is "equal-mindedness." The word now means "composure; evenness of mind or temper." Some other words based on the same root are listed below.

egalitarian	equate	equilibrium	iniquitous
equable	equidistant	inequity	unequivocal

From the list of words above, choose the one that corresponds to each of the brief definitions below. Write the word in the blank space in the illustrative sentence below the definition. Use an online or print dictionary if necessary.

1. asserting or promoting social, political, or economic equality; advocating the removal of inequalities among people

Most utopian societies are envisioned as _____.

2. equally separated from a given point or location

The two suburbs are _____ from St. Louis.

3. to regard or treat as equivalent; to make equal, equalize

It's a mistake to _____ politeness with kindness.

4. an act or situation of injustice and unfairness

A society based on _____ is ripe for revolution.

5. wicked, very unjust, vicious

The former dictator was tried for _____ deeds.

6. clear, plain, absolute, certain

There was no mistaking his _____ refusal to compromise.

7. uniform, marked by lack of noticeable or extreme variation; steady

Los Angeles is famous for its _____ climate.

8. balance (*"equal balance"*)

It's not easy to maintain one's _____ in a difficult situation.

*Read the following selection, taking note of the **boldface** words and their contexts. These words are among those you will be studying in Unit 13. As you complete the exercises in this unit, it may help to refer to the way the words are used below.*

Ansel Adams
<Essay>

Jeffrey Pine, Sentinel Dome, Yosemite National Park, California © 1940 by Ansel Adams

For someone celebrated today as one of America's greatest photographers, Ansel Adams had an **inauspicious** start in life. He was just 4 years old when much of his native city, San Francisco, was destroyed by the earthquake and fire of 1906. That day, a strong aftershock pushed young Ansel into a brick wall with such force that it broke his nose, which remained crooked for the rest of his life. One year later, the loss of the family fortune in a financial panic left his mother **disconsolate** and distant from her son. Hindered by dyslexia as a student, Adams barely kept his head above water in school. As a teen, his shyness and social awkwardness resulted in a relatively solitary adolescence.

Fortunately, Adams found great joy and inspiration in music and nature. A self-taught pianist, he set aside regular schooling to follow his passion for music. The discipline and structure that his musical studies demanded **buttressed** his otherwise restless youth. But it was nature itself which became his **incontrovertible** muse. Adams fell in love with the Sierra Nevada mountains on his first visit, in 1916. He returned to the Yosemite Valley, the jewel of this mountain range along California's eastern border, every year of his life. On that first trip, Adams's father gave his son a camera, a gift that would **abet** a life devoted to nature and to art.

Three years later, the seventeen-year-old Adams joined the Sierra Club, a new organization dedicated to preserving natural resources and nature's unique treasures. This proved to be an **opportune** decision, as the group's leaders wished to **foment** a strong conservation movement and needed Adams's assistance. Part of their plan was to have a photographer document the Sierra Club's adventure outings, and members **broached** the idea to the boy who seemed always to have a camera in tow. The delighted young photographer agreed and soon Adams became a **connoisseur** of the Sierra landscape—Yosemite in particular—while honing his skills as a visual artist. Adams and the Sierra Club were good for each other: The photographer's **prolific** output not only lured new supporters to the environmental cause, but Adams himself found a platform for his artistic vision—celebrating the glories of nature.

The competent pianist evolved into a gifted photographer. Ansel Adams's keen eye spurred him on to master the technical aspects of his new love. He arrived each year at Yosemite **encumbered** with unwieldy photographic gear, notebooks, and maps. He was willing to toil **herculean** hours if the effort helped improve his skills. Yet, despite a rigorous workload, he would allow himself the occasional harmless **carousal** with his ever-widening circle of friends and colleagues.

Adams was a driven man. He traveled the country photographing, lecturing, and writing. As an enthusiastic promoter of photography as a fine art, he helped establish the nation's first museum department of photography at the Museum of Modern Art in New York. And he remained a committed activist for preserving the wilderness. His dedication to the National Park system and vigorous support of the major environmental causes never abated.

Ansel Adams, 1961

While some critics noted an "absence of humanity" in Ansel Adams's landscape photographs—for his photographs celebrated nature, not mankind—his **rejoinder** was that his work continued the tradition of Thomas Cole, Frederic Church, Albert Bierstadt, and other nineteenth-century Romantic painters who sought to imbue the splendors of nature with an emotional and inspirational majesty. Everyone benefited from such a vision: At a time of indifference to, if not **blatant** disregard for, the nation's natural resources, seeing the places Adams captured so beautifully in photographs motivated Americans to preserve them for all time.

Thanks to Ansel Adams, those who might never visit the glorious Yosemite National Park can still experience the drama of its beauty. The enduring appreciation for Adams's photos is largely due to his insistence upon high-quality images **collated** in what might be called "coffee-table books." This idea let him straddle the worlds of fine art photography, environmental education, and popular culture. Through money earned by the national parks and environmental groups from selling calendars, books, and other items featuring his exquisite photographs, even in death Adams has continued to benefit the rugged land he loved and championed.

Snap the code, or go to
vocabularyworkshop.com

Definitions

Note the spelling, pronunciation, part(s) of speech, and definition(s) of each of the following words. Then write the word in the blank spaces in the illustrative sentence(s) following. Finally, study the lists of synonyms and antonyms.

1. abet
(ə bet′)

(*v.*) to encourage, assist, aid, support (especially in something wrong or unworthy)

To allow a man in his condition to get behind the wheel of a car is to _____ a potential crime.

ANTONYMS: hamper, hinder, impede, frustrate

2. aver
(ə vər′)

(*v.*) to affirm, declare confidently

I will _____ your fitness to do the work to any prospective employer who inquires.

SYNONYMS: assert, asseverate, avouch
ANTONYMS: deny, repudiate, disclaim

3. blatant
(blā′ tənt)

(*adj.*) noisy in a coarse, offensive way; obvious or conspicuous, especially in an unfavorable sense

Your comments showed a _____ disregard for my feelings.

SYNONYMS: flagrant, glaring, egregious, disagreeably loud
ANTONYMS: inconsequential, trifling, piddling, petty

4. broach
(brōch)

(*v.*) to bring up or begin to talk about (a subject); to announce, introduce; to break the surface of the water; to turn sideways to the wind and waves; to pierce (a keg or cask) in order to draw off liquid; (*n.*) a spit for roasting; a tool for tapping casks

She opted not to _____ the subject of the moldy smell in the bedroom for fear of insulting her hosts.

5. buttress
(bə′ trəs)

(*v.*) to support, prop up, strengthen; (*n.*) a supporting structure

He has read so widely that he can produce facts to _____ any argument he advances.

I had to add _____ on either side of my rickety shed to keep it from collapsing.

SYNONYMS: (*v.*) bolster, reinforce, brace, shore up
ANTONYMS: (*v.*) undermine, weaken, impair

6. carousal
(kə raủ′ zəl)

(*n.*) noisy revelry or merrymaking (often with a suggestion of heavy drinking)

Vikings are notorious for having enjoyed a _____ after each of their battles.

SYNONYMS: binge, jamboree

7. collate
(kō' lāt)

(*v.*) to compare critically in order to note differences, similarities, etc.; to arrange in order for some specific purpose

We decided to _____ the recipes according to how complicated they are.

SYNONYMS: sort out, cross-check

8. connoisseur
(kän ə sər')

(*n.*) an expert; one who is well qualified to pass critical judgments, especially in one of the fine arts

She was a _____ of both music and film.

SYNONYMS: savant, pundit; ANTONYMS: ignoramus, philistine

9. disconsolate
(dis kän' sə lət)

(*adj.*) deeply unhappy or dejected; without hope, beyond consolation

Macbeth hardly seems _____ when his wife dies; instead, he bluntly says he has no time to grieve.

SYNONYMS: grief-stricken, inconsolable
ANTONYMS: cheerful, blithe, buoyant, jaunty

10. encumber
(in kəm' bər)

(*v.*) to weigh down or burden (with difficulties, cares, debt, etc.); to fill up, block up, hinder

I feared that joining another club would

_____ me with too many obligations.

SYNONYMS: overload, clog; ANTONYMS: unburden, unload, relieve

11. foment
(fō ment')

(*v.*) to promote trouble or rebellion; to apply warm liquids to, warm

Toward the end of the film, the peasant leader attempts to

_____ a storming of the scientist's castle.

SYNONYMS: instigate, incite, stir up
ANTONYMS: quell, quash, squelch, suppress

12. grisly
(griz' lē)

(*adj.*) frightful, horrible, ghastly

Katherine Anne Porter's *Pale Horse, Pale Rider* reveals the

_____ effects of the influenza virus during the epidemic that followed World War I.

SYNONYMS: gruesome, gory; ANTONYMS: pleasant, delightful

13. herculean
(hər kyü lē' ən)

(*adj.*) (*capital H*) relating to Hercules; (*lowercase h*) characterized by great strength; very hard to do in the sense of requiring unusual strength

We saw that getting the huge desk up the stairs would require a _____ effort.

SYNONYMS: mighty, powerful, arduous, onerous
ANTONYMS: puny, Lilliputian, bantam

14. impassive
(im pas′ iv)

(*adj.*) showing no feeling or emotion; inanimate; motionless

Since nervous laughter is the sign of an inexperienced actor, I tried to adopt an _____ expression on stage.

SYNONYMS: emotionless, stoical, insensible
ANTONYMS: emotional, passionate, excitable

15. inauspicious
(in ô spish′ əs)

(*adj.*) unfavorable, unlucky, suggesting bad luck for the future

Our road trip got off to an _____ start when we ran out of gas within five miles of home.

SYNONYMS: unpropitious, unpromising, untimely
ANTONYMS: propitious, favorable

16. incontrovertible
(in kän trə vər′ tə bəl)

(*adj.*) unquestionable, beyond dispute

The document was remarkable for its tact yet also _____ in its facts.

SYNONYMS: incontestable, indisputable, indubitable
ANTONYMS: debatable, dubious, open to question

17. nonplussed
(nän pləst′)

(*adj.*, *part.*) puzzled, not knowing what to do, at a loss

She thought she was prepared for all contingencies, but she was _____ by the turn of events.

SYNONYMS: perplexed, stumped, flabbergasted
ANTONYMS: poised, confident, assured

18. opportune
(äp ər tün′)

(*adj.*) suitable or convenient for a particular purpose; occurring at an appropriate time

If you intend to give that dog a bath, you had better pick an _____ moment, and then pounce!

SYNONYMS: timely, appropriate, felicitous
ANTONYMS: untimely, inconvenient, inappropriate

19. prolific
(pro lif′ ik)

(*adj.*) abundantly productive; abundant, profuse

Haydn was a more _____ composer than Mozart, in part because he lived much longer.

SYNONYMS: fruitful, fecund, proliferous
ANTONYMS: barren, unproductive, sterile, sparse

20. rejoinder
(ri join′ dər)

(*n.*) a reply to a reply, especially from the defendant in a legal suit

When he explained where he had been and what he had done, her _____ was sharp and critical.

SYNONYMS: reply, response, riposte, retort

Choosing the Right Word

*Select the **boldface** word that better completes each sentence. You might refer to the selection on pages 164–165 to see how most of these words are used in context.*

1. Very few poems by Emily Dickinson were published during her lifetime, but she was nevertheless a (**disconsolate, prolific**) poet, writing over 1,700 poems.

2. You will never be able to complete this challenging hike if you (**encumber, collate**) yourself with so much "essential equipment."

3. What we need is not opinions or "educated guesses" but (**impassive, incontrovertible**) proof that can stand up under the closest examination.

4. Although police identified the perpetrator using fingerprints, DNA, *and* video footage, he (**inauspiciously, blatantly**) denied that he had committed the crime.

Emily Dickinson's unconventional use of punctuation and capitalization was considered eccentric in her time.

5. When they offered to help him, he proudly (**averred, abetted**) that he could handle the situation on his own.

6. If you are going to wait for an occasion that seems (**opportune, grisly**) in *every* respect, then in all probability you will have to wait forever.

7. What could be more (**herculean, disconsolate**) than the long drive home on a rainy night after we had lost the championship game by one point!

8. His parents are such sensitive people that I'm not at all sure how I should (**broach, foment**) the news of his injury to them.

9. I don't know anything about quiches and soufflés, but I'm a true (**buttress, connoisseur**) when it comes to pizza.

10. The opening of our show took place most (**inauspiciously, opportunely**) in the midst of a transit strike and a record-breaking snowstorm.

11. Cleaning up the old beach house seemed an almost impossible task, but she attacked it with (**herculean, disconsolate**) energy.

12. I still cannot figure out how to get my printer to (**collate, buttress**) pages automatically when I want to make multiple copies of a document.

13. Isn't it ridiculous to say that the disorder was (**nonplussed, fomented**) by outsiders when we all know that it resulted from bad conditions inside the institution?

14. Dr. Slavin's original diagnosis, although questioned by several colleagues, was strongly (**buttressed, fomented**) by the results of the laboratory tests.

15. I was so (**impassive, nonplussed**) when my acting partner forgot his lines and stared blankly at the audience that I, too, had trouble remembering my dialogue.

16. I know that he is wealthy and comes from a prominent family, but does that status excuse his (**blatant, nonplussed**) disregard of good manners?

17. In spite of her long and (**grisly, prolific**) career, her reputation today rests entirely on one great play.

18. I like a good time as much as anyone, but I don't think that the celebration of our nation's birthday should become a rowdy (**carousal, rejoinder**).

19. I wasn't so much surprised at not getting the job as I was (**encumbered, nonplussed**) by his strange explanation that I was "overqualified."

20. I truly felt that reality could never be as horrible as the (**impassive, grisly**) phantoms that were disturbing my dreams.

21. With tireless patience, the wily detective (**encumbered, collated**) bits and pieces of evidence until he gained an insight into how the crime had been committed.

22. Psychologists tell us that people who seem to be unusually (**impassive, blatant**) are often the ones most likely to lose control of their emotions in times of stress.

23. Well-meaning but misguided friends (**abetted, averred**) his plans to run away to Hollywood and "become a movie star."

24. The speaker's inept replies to questions from the floor were met with a barrage of indignant (**carousals, rejoinders**).

25. Her many blue ribbons prove she is a (**connoisseur, herculean**) of baking.

Synonyms

*Choose the word from this unit that is the same or most nearly the same in meaning as the **boldface** word or expression in the phrase. Write that word on the line. Use a dictionary if necessary.*

1. profess his undying love   _____

2. was **heartbroken** after the tragedy   _____

3. gave a conciliatory **answer**   _____

4. endorse her sleazy scheme   _____

5. carefully **rearranged** files   _____

6. baffled by the answer   _____

7. her **unemotional** response to the tragedy   _____

8. hampered with cares and troubles   _____

9. a **colossal** challenge   _____

10. horrendous evidence of the wreck   _____

Antonyms

*Choose the word from this unit that is most nearly opposite in meaning to the **boldface** word or expression in the phrase. Write that word on the line. Use a dictionary if necessary.*

1. an opera with a **lovely** conclusion _____

2. his open, **expressive** face _____

3. a **haphazard** pile of unpaid bills _____

4. exhibiting a **knowing** attitude _____

5. **disavow** an earlier statement _____

Completing the Sentence

From the words in this unit, choose the one that best completes each of the following sentences. Write the word in the space provided.

1. The mangled bodies of the victims told their own _____ story of what had happened.

2. The testimony of three different witnesses, all confirming the same basic facts, made the guilt of the accused _____.

3. Although we have had our disagreements, I will _____ now that she has always been scrupulously honest in her dealings with me.

4. The towering walls of many medieval cathedrals are prevented from falling down by huge "flying _____" on the outsides of the buildings.

5. She is so _____ with family obligations that she rarely has a free moment for herself.

6. Aren't you exaggerating when you suggest that the job of stock clerk calls for someone with _____ strength?

7. The New Year's Eve party started off quietly enough, but it soon became a full-fledged _____.

8. I don't think you can really accuse the producers of _____ favoritism simply because they chose a friend for the title role.

9. If the pages aren't _____ properly, they'll be out of proper sequence when our class magazine is bound.

10. I was utterly _____ when I realized that football practice and the rehearsal for the class show were at the same time.

11. I know you are really disappointed at not getting that job, but don't allow yourself to feel so _____ that you won't have the energy to look for another.

12. I will not in any way _____ their plans to play a cruel and humiliating trick on an unoffending person.

13. When I saw the worried expression on the face of my employer, I realized that it wasn't a(n) _____ time to ask for a raise.

14. It would be impossible to _____ ethnic discord in a school where students of different backgrounds understand and respect one another.

15. One need not be a(n) _____ of modern dance to recognize that Martha is exceptionally talented in that field.

16. The big game had a truly _____ start for us when our star quarterback fumbled and lost the ball on the first play.

17. Now that you mention it, I don't think that "Sez you" was a particularly effective _____ to her trenchant and insightful criticisms of your proposal.

18. He is such a(n) _____ writer that his books occupy almost an entire shelf in the school library.

19. Although she remained outwardly _____ during the trial, I could sense the emotional turmoil beneath the surface.

20. "When I first _____ this topic two years ago," I observed, "my ideas were met with indifference and some skepticism."

Writing: Words in Action

1. Look back at "Ansel Adams" (pages 164–165). Imagine that you work for a fine arts museum that is preparing a large exhibition of Ansel Adams's photographs. Your task is to seek funding. Write a fund-raising letter explaining why the museum wants to present an extensive new exhibition of Adams's works. Provide at least three reasons that Adams deserves a major exhibition. Use at least two details from the passage and three unit words.

2. *"Could a greater miracle take place than for us to look through each other's eyes for an instant?"* —Henry David Thoreau, from Walden

Think about Thoreau's question. How important is it to try to view the world from a different perspective? Write an essay in which you explain what Thoreau's quotation means, and explore a few ways that people can learn to "look through each other's eyes." Support your essay with specific details, examples from your own life, your studies, and the reading (pages 164–165). Write at least three paragraphs, and use three or more words from this unit.

Vocabulary in Context

Literary Text

The following excerpts are from The Memoirs of Margaret Fuller Ossoli, Volume I. *Some of the words you have studied in this unit appear in **boldface** type. Complete each statement below the excerpt by circling the letter of the correct answer.*

1. She had a taste for gems, ciphers, talismans, omens, coincidences, and birthdays. She had a special love for the planet Jupiter, and a belief that the month of September was **inauspicious** to her.

If something is **inauspicious**, it is NOT

a. unusual
b. obscure
c. lucky
d. inconsequential

2. Margaret suffered no vice to insult her presence, but called the offender to instant account, when the law of right or of beauty was violated.... Others might **abet** a crime by silence, if they pleased; she chose to clear herself of all complicity, by calling the act by its name.

To **abet** a crime is to

a. explain it
b. support it
c. hide it
d. publicize it

3. Man present in nature, commanding nature too sternly to be inspired by it, standing like the rock amid the sea, or moving like the fire over the land, either **impassive**, or irresistible; knowing not the soft mediums or fine flights of life, but by the force which he expresses, piercing to the center.

Something that is **impassive** is

a. indifferent
b. memorable
c. gracious
d. productive

4. In the description, by a **connoisseur**, of this picture, read to me while I was looking at it, it is spoken of as in Raphael's first manner, cold, hard, trammeled. But to me how did that face proclaim the Infinite Love!

Margaret Fuller, a nineteenth-century teacher, translator, and critic, wrote a book in defense of women's rights.

Someone who is a **connoisseur** is

a. a pioneer
b. an artist
c. a specialist
d. an amateur

5. Margaret spoke well...but I remember that she seemed **encumbered**, or interrupted, by the headiness or incapacity of the men, whom she had not had the advantage of training....

A person who is **encumbered** is

a. calm and relaxed
b. highly trained
c. sad and anxious
d. weighed down

Snap the code, or go to
vocabularyworkshop.com

*Read the following selection, taking note of the **boldface** words and their contexts. These words are among those you will be studying in Unit 14. As you complete the exercises in this unit, it may help to refer to the way the words are used below.*

Revolutionary Women
<Historical Nonfiction>

During the American Revolution, myriad colonial-era women, stirred by patriotic fervor, were not **amenable** to continuing their customary roles in the home. Instead, from the **inception** of the conflict, they influenced the trajectory of the war. The following is an account of a handful of these notable women.

For Mercy Otis Warren of Massachusetts, the pen was mightier than the sword; in the early 1770s, as tensions between England and the colonies escalated, Warren put her writing aptitude to work for the Patriots. One of her

plays, *The Adulateur* (1772) **berated** Massachusetts's royal governor, while two others, *The Defeat* (1773) and *The Group* (1775), attacked Loyalists—colonists loyal to England. Warren's plays were reprinted in newspapers and converted many people living in the colonies to the Patriot cause.

Dicey Langston, only fifteen years old and a girl, seemed an improbable spy; yet for months this **precocious** South Carolinian outwitted the Loyalist troops encamped around her family's plantation. Langston surreptitiously relayed vital information to Patriot militias encamped in the countryside, and one night she traveled twenty miles on a **tortuous** country path and crossed a **turgid** stream to warn the militia of a Loyalist attack. Their attack thwarted, the Loyalists finally determined that Langston was a spy and **sadistically** attempted to shoot her father, but Langston shielded him with her body and **supplicated** with the soldiers to shoot her first. The soldiers, impressed with her bravery, let both Langstons live.

Not every woman of the Revolution was a Patriot. Flora MacDonald was born in Scotland and achieved notoriety by saving the life of "Bonnie Prince Charlie," a Scottish royal who aspired to the throne of England. MacDonald retained her **obdurate** support for the monarchy even after emigrating to North Carolina with her husband in 1774. She helped raise a Loyalist unit to fight the Patriots, but at the Battle of Moores Creek Bridge the Loyalists lost. The **carnage** was horrific and MacDonald's husband was

Mercy Otis Warren, circa 1763

Mrs. Schuyler Burning Her Wheat Fields on the Approach of the British, by EG Leutze, 1852

imprisoned, so MacDonald, with her resources **depleted**, moved to Canada.

Some women of the Revolution, such as Catherine Schuyler, were saboteurs who deprived the invading army of supplies. Schuyler ignited the wheat fields on her land in upstate New York in 1777, when a voracious British army was approaching from Canada. Schuyler elected not to feed this **extraneous** force, but deciding to burn the wheat must have been difficult, for there was no **surfeit** of food in the colonies.

Women were excluded from the army, but a number of women masqueraded as men to serve in the Continental army. The identity of one, a woman from Maine, is unknown

although she served until war's end; but another, Ann Bailey of Massachusetts, was found out after just three weeks. Bailey was fined and imprisoned for her deception, her record stating: "Discharged. Being a woman dressed in men's cloths." (sic) Sally St. Clair enlisted with her boyfriend and died during a British siege in Georgia. One of the best-known cases of a woman serving in the army is that of Deborah Sampson, who as "Robert Shurtliff" fought courageously and met all the **criteria** of a good soldier for eighteen months. A doctor treating her for an **infirmity** discovered her secret, but Sampson received an honorable discharge and even a pension for her service. Later she **expatiated** on her experiences during a lecture tour of her native New England.

Line engraving depicting Deborah Sampson as a soldier in the Continental army

iWords

Snap the code, or go to **vocabularyworkshop.com**

Definitions

Note the spelling, pronunciation, part(s) of speech, and definition(s) of each of the following words. Then write the word in the blank spaces in the illustrative sentence(s) following. Finally, study the lists of synonyms and antonyms.

1. amenable
(ə mē′ nə bəl)

(*adj.*) willing to follow advice or authority, tractable, submissive; responsive; liable to be held responsible

They will be _____ to your instructions as long as what you say makes sense.

SYNONYMS: agreeable, compliant, docile
ANTONYMS: unresponsive, resistant, recalcitrant

2. berate
(bi rāt′)

(*v.*) to scold sharply

He removed the dog from obedience school when he discovered that the instructors had _____ it too harshly.

SYNONYMS: chide, rebuke, reprove, reprimand
ANTONYMS: praise, compliment, pat on the back

3. carnage
(kär′ nəj)

(*n.*) large-scale slaughter or loss of life

Until television began to broadcast footage of war, the _____ of battle was rarely made real to far-off civilian populations.

SYNONYMS: butchery, bloodbath, massacre

4. credulous
(krej′ ə ləs)

(*adj.*) too ready to believe, easily deceived

Though he was no dolt, his _____ nature and desire to believe the best of people made him quite easy to deceive.

SYNONYMS: gullible, trusting; ANTONYMS: dubious, skeptical

5. criterion
(pl., **criteria**)
(krī tir′ ē ən)

(*n.*) a rule, test; a standard for judgment or evaluation

She was disturbed to discover that the _____ for the award was based on style, not substance.

SYNONYMS: yardstick, touchstone, gauge, canon

6. deplete
(di plēt′)

(*v.*) to use up as a result of spending or consumption; to diminish greatly

Dwelling on all that could go wrong with your project will _____ your energy and courage.

SYNONYMS: exhaust, empty, drain, bankrupt
ANTONYMS: replenish, refill, restock, resupply

7. expatiate
(ek spā' shē āt)

(*v.*) to expand on, write or talk at length or in detail; to move about freely

We would like you to _____ on the interesting matters you only touched upon earlier today.

SYNONYMS: elaborate, enlarge, descant, wander, roam
ANTONYMS: sketch roughly, summarize, condense, adumbrate

8. extraneous
(ek strā' nē əs)

(*adj.*) coming from the outside, foreign; present but not essential, irrelevant

One handy way to dodge a difficult question is to earnestly begin talking about something _____ to it.

SYNONYMS: incidental, extrinsic, adventitious
ANTONYMS: intrinsic, relevant, pertinent, germane

9. inception
(in sep' shən)

(*n.*) the beginning, start, earliest stage of some process, institution, etc.

He has worked here steadily since the firm's _____ and knows every facet of the job.

SYNONYMS: commencement, inauguration, outset
ANTONYMS: completion, conclusion, termination

10. infirmity
(in fərm' ə tē)

(*n.*) a weakness or ailment (physical, mental, moral, etc.)

Was his "deafness" an _____ of old age or a lack of interest in the conversation?

SYNONYMS: affliction, malady, defect

11. jejune
(ji jün')

(*adj.*) lacking in nutritive value; lacking in interest or substance; immature, juvenile

My favorite teacher turned history from a _____ study of the distant past into a relevant topic of discussion.

SYNONYMS: puerile, childish; ANTONYMS: stimulating, mature

12. obdurate
(äb' dyü rət)

(*adj.*) stubborn, unyielding

Vincent van Gogh was _____ in painting whatever he wished, even when no one would buy his work.

SYNONYMS: obstinate, adamant; ANTONYMS: tractable, flexible

13. potpourri
(pō pü rē')

(*n.*) a collection of diverse or miscellaneous items; a general mixture; petals mixed with spices for scent

The furniture was a _____ of hand-me-downs from my father's parents and my stepmother's aunt.

SYNONYMS: hodgepodge, farrago, medley
ANTONYMS: homogeneous or uniform group

14. precocious
(pri kō′ shəs)

(*adj.*) showing unusually early development (especially in talents and mental capacity)

She showed a _____ talent for science.

SYNONYMS: gifted, advanced; ANTONYMS: backward, slow

15. sadistic
(sə dis′ tik)

(*adj.*) delighting in cruelty, excessively cruel

The Geneva Convention of 1949 outlawed torture and _____ treatment of prisoners of war.

SYNONYMS: brutal, vicious, inhuman, fiendish
ANTONYMS: masochistic, clement, humane, merciful

16. sententious
(sen ten′ shəs)

(*adj.*) self-righteous, characterized by moralizing; given to use of maxims or adages; saying much in few words, pithy

The _____ advice, though wise, was too general to help their particular situation.

SYNONYMS: aphoristic, epigrammatic, moralistic
ANTONYMS: discursive, diffuse, episodic

17. supplicate
(səp′ lə kāt)

(*v.*) to beg earnestly and humbly

He chose to _____ for mercy not on his own account, but so that his wife would not suffer.

SYNONYMS: plead, petition, implore

18. surfeit
(sər′ fət)

(*n.*) an excess or overindulgence, as in eating or drinking, causing disgust; (*v.*) to feed or supply with anything to excess

A _____ of food, drink, and clowning puts Shakespeare's Falstaff in disgrace with the King.

SYNONYMS: (*n.*) glut; (*v.*) satiate; ANTONYMS: (*n.*) dearth, paucity

19. tortuous
(tôr′ chü əs)

(*adj.*) winding, twisted, crooked; highly involved, complex; devious

The cameras had to be portable in order to follow the athletes up the narrow and _____ path to the summit.

SYNONYMS: circuitous, serpentine, labyrinthine
ANTONYMS: direct, straight, straightforward

20. turgid
(tər′ jid)

(*adj.*) swollen, bloated, filled to excess; overdecorated or excessive language

The heavy rains turned the fields swampy and the river _____.

SYNONYMS: inflated, pompous, bombastic
ANTONYMS: understated, unadorned, austere

Choosing the Right Word

*Select the **boldface** word that better completes each sentence. You might refer to the selection on pages 174–175 to see how most of these words are used in context.*

1. Although *Gone with the Wind* won a Pulitzer Prize, critics often (**berate, expatiate**) the novel for its stereotypical portrayals of African Americans.

2. In the poems and prayers of many ancient cultures, human beings (**expatiate, supplicate**) their deities for mercy and aid.

3. Our dean is a strict disciplinarian, but I have always found her (**amenable, turgid**) to reasonable requests.

4. A well-known actor submitted his poems to a publisher, who deemed the verses (**precocious, jejune**) and tedious.

5. Given the kinds of tools the ancient Egyptians had to work with, the construction of the pyramids was an extraordinarily (**precocious, jejune**) feat of engineering.

6. The (**infirmity, carnage**) caused each year by careless driving has become a major national scandal.

7. What disturbs the coach is not that Tom called the wrong play but that he refuses (**obdurately, precociously**) to admit that he made a mistake.

Margaret Mitchell wrote a newspaper column in the *Atlanta Journal* before writing her world-famous novel, *Gone with the Wind.*

8. Some journalists find researching materials in a library a (**tortuous, credulous**) task, preferring to sit and let their computers do the work.

9. Passengers who are stranded on airplanes and forced to sit on the tarmac for hours may begin to think of airlines as (**amenable, sadistic**) agencies.

10. Since its (**carnage, inception**), the electric guitar has been a symbol of innovation, energy, and rebellion.

11. Few things are more tragic than to see a great mind fall victim to a serious (**inception, infirmity**).

12. You cannot dismiss everything he says as (**obdurate, jejune**) simply because he is young and lacks experience of the world.

13. Although he (**expatiates, supplicates**) fluently on the need for a new community action program, I have yet to see him do anything to bring it about.

14. In his efforts to impress moral principles on the children, he made use of (**tortuous, sententious**) formulas, such as "To be good, do good."

15. The sales manager said she would apply only one (**criterion, carnage**) when assessing my plan for an advertising campaign: "Will it sell more mouthwash?"

16. I think the class show will be much more effective if it has a constant theme running through it, instead of being just a (**potpourri, surfeit**) of songs, dances, and sketches.

17. Instead of constantly (**berating, depleting)** the children, why don't you try to explain quietly and clearly how you expect them to behave?

18. My rules for effective writing are, "Emphasize what is essential, play down what is secondary, eliminate what is (**extraneous, turgid**)."

19. The prolonged drought has so (**depleted, berated**) the supplies in our reservoir that we may have to consider rationing water.

20. At the very (**inception, criterion**) of my career, I set the goals and adopted the basic strategies that were to guide me through many years of outstanding success.

21. His (**obdurate, turgid**) conversation, with its exaggerated adjectives and far-fetched figures of speech, made me realize once and for all the virtues of plain speaking.

22. Although he is not given to physical maltreatment, I think there is a truly (**precocious, sadistic**) element in his willingness to humiliate people by belittling them in public.

23. She tried to justify the lies she had told us, but I was unable to follow her (**amenable, tortuous**) explanation.

24. Vic is so (**sententious, credulous**) that he actually believed me when I said that I had invented an automatic composition-writing machine.

25. I have had my (**surfeit, carnage**) of excuses and evasions; now I want action.

 Synonyms

*Choose the word from this unit that is the same or most nearly the same in meaning as the **boldface** word or expression in the phrase. Write that word on the line. Use a dictionary if necessary.*

1. an **insipid** view of history _____

2. the **overblown** rhetoric of the politician _____

3. **entreat** the captain on behalf of her son _____

4. a **meandering**, complicated plot _____

5. a **didactic** way of addressing the group _____

6. too **naive** to perceive trickery _____

7. a **mélange** of spices _____

8. was present at the product **launch** _____

9. not **acquiescent** to that idea _____

10. a **guideline** by which to judge the entries _____

Antonyms

*Choose the word from this unit that is most nearly opposite in meaning to the **boldface** word or expression in the phrase. Write that word on the line. Use a dictionary if necessary.*

1. bored by the **wordy** presentation   _____

2. a **sophisticated** sense of humor   _____

3. a **lack of variety** in the show's acts   _____

4. thought the décor too **plain**   _____

5. too **perceptive** for her own good   _____

Completing the Sentence

From the words in this unit, choose the one that best completes each of the following sentences. Write the word in the space provided.

1. Although I ask no special consideration for myself, I am not too proud to _____ on behalf of my children.

2. The more _____ you are, the easier it will be for swindlers and con artists to hoodwink you.

3. Usefulness is not the only _____ for including words in this book, but it is the primary one.

4. In spite of all our efforts to appeal to whatever human sympathies the kidnappers might have, they remained _____.

5. Her instructions told me exactly what I wanted to know, without a single _____ detail.

6. Our reading program this term is a delightful _____ of stories, essays, poetry, and drama from many different periods.

7. My last date turned out to be such an expensive affair that my funds were sadly _____ for the rest of the month.

8. The stream followed a(n) _____ course as it twisted through the broken countryside.

9. When my stubborn younger brother proved so _____ to my request, I began to suspect that he had some special reason for wanting to please me.

10. The simple and austere prose of the Gettysburg Address stands in stark contrast to the _____ and overblown rhetoric of a great many other nineteenth-century orations.

11. Although he announces piously how much it hurts him to punish people, I think he takes a(n) _____ pleasure in it.

12. Wouldn't you agree that TV has been _____ lately with sitcoms and reality shows?

13. When I asked him why he wasn't going to the prom, he answered in his usual _____ style, "No dough, no dance!"

14. You deserve to be severely _____ for your misbehavior during such a solemn ceremony.

15. "How do you expect your mind to grow when you feed it solely on the _____ pap that comes out of the television?" I asked pointedly.

16. It is difficult to imagine the _____ that would result from an all-out war fought with nuclear weapons.

17. One of the benefits I gained from my summer job in the new hospital was learning to be patient with people suffering from various types of _____.

18. It's painful to have to listen to him _____ on his own virtues when I'm dying to give some fascinating details about my own life and accomplishments.

19. Any child who can read at the age of three must be considered remarkably _____.

20. At the very _____ of his administration, the new president announced a list of the objectives he hoped to accomplish.

Writing: Words in Action

1. Look back at "Revolutionary Women" (pages 174–175). Think about how contemporaries of the revolutionary women might have reacted to the women's bold actions during a time of war. Write an editorial from the perspective of a woman of the time in which you express your opinions—pro or con— about the actions of the revolutionary women mentioned in the passage. Use at least two details from the passage and three unit words.

2. Today, women in most Western countries can serve in the military, but many nations—including the United States—still have prohibitions against allowing women to serve in direct combat. In a brief argumentative essay, state and support your opinion about whether female soldiers should be allowed to participate in combat alongside men. Support your argument with specific details, your observations and studies, and the reading (pages 174–175). Write at least three paragraphs, and use three or more words from this unit.

Vocabulary in Context

Literary Text

The following excerpts are from Bleak House *and* Our Mutual Friend *by Charles Dickens. Some of the words you have studied in this unit appear in* **boldface** *type. Complete each statement below the excerpt by circling the letter of the correct answer.*

1. Besides the melancholy boy...there were two other boys and one dirty little limp girl in a gauzy dress. Such a **precocious** little girl, with such a dowdy bonnet on (that, too, of a gauzy texture), who brought her sandalled shoes in an old threadbare velvet reticule. (*Bleak House*)

   A **precocious** child is
   a. dirty and dowdy
   b. shy and wary
   c. mature beyond her years
   d. beloved by all

2. ...[W]ith a great many people in a great many instances, the question is never one of a change from wrong to right (which is quite an **extraneous** consideration), but is always one of injury or advantage.... (*Bleak House*)

   An **extraneous** consideration is
   a. superfluous
   b. dreary
   c. essential
   d. rewarding

Patrick Kennedy and Carey Mulligan in the 2005 miniseries *Bleak House*

3. The **credulous** little creature again embraced Mrs. Lammle most affectionately, and then held out her hand to Mr. Lammle. (*Our Mutual Friend*)

   Someone who is **credulous** is
   a. influential
   b. naive
   c. cynical
   d. feeble

4. "Yes or no, and no half measures!" was the motto which that **obdurate** person many times repeated; shaking his fist at Mr. Boffin, and pegging his motto into the floor with his wooden leg, in a threatening and alarming manner. (*Our Mutual Friend*)

   An **obdurate** person is NOT
   a. sorrowful
   b. staunch
   c. obstinate
   d. compliant

5. The Six Jolly Fellowship Porters, already mentioned as a tavern of a dropsical appearance, had long settled down into a state of hale **infirmity**. In its whole constitution it had not a straight floor, and hardly a straight line; but it had outlasted...many a better-trimmed building, many a sprucer public-house. (*Our Mutual Friend*)

   A tavern in a state of **infirmity** looks
   a. dilapidated
   b. organized
   c. new
   d. vacant

Interactive Quiz

Snap the code, or go to
vocabularyworkshop.com

*Read the following selection, taking note of the **boldface** words and their contexts. These words are among those you will be studying in Unit 15. As you complete the exercises in this unit, it may help to refer to the way the words are used below.*

New Tribe Discovered in Amazon
<Newspaper Article>

by Humberto Ronaldo Fonseca
PORTO VELHO, Brazil

Brazilian officials have released photographs of an extremely isolated tribe living deep in the Amazon rainforest in western Brazil. The images show a community of approximately 150 people with a proud and fearless **demeanor**. The photos also indicate that the tribe has metal goods, such as a machete knife and a pan, and **sartorial** tools such as needles and thimbles. It is likely these items were acquired through inter-tribal trading of goods or resources, experts say. They believe the people shown in the photographs are descendants of tribes that retreated into the jungle a century ago. Christine Morris, of the travel-adventure magazine *Exploring,* took the photographs. Tribal advocates see the release of such photos as a tool to **thwart** illegal logging. Many Brazilian tribes use the jungle as a **bulwark** against contact with the modern world.

Little **definitive** information is known about the day-to-day ways of this and other indigenous people, according to Amazon Today (AT). The group is expert on **enigmatic** tribes so isolated that their members only recently come in contact with outsiders, although many are aware of airplanes

from overflights. AT's Web site counters notions of indigenous tribes as primitive survivors. "Everyone has neighbors, even when they're some distance away, and they'll know who their neighbors are. No man is an island," says the group's Web site. Amazon Today is **adamant** that the tribes "are not backward or 'Stone Age'; they just live differently."

Anthropologists, propelled by **presentiment**, have attempted to study the disappearing tribes. Many of tribes, like the one just photographed, move easily throughout a vast area and adapt to new locations due to the region's consistent climate, which means plants and animals are alike throughout. The common environment accounts for a similarity in customs and lifestyles among Amazonian tribes, according to Maria Teresa Santiago, the head of outreach at Amazon Today.

The nomadic tribes move from place to place, often in boats made of hollowed tree trunks that they propel with hand-made paddles, experts say. The people survive by hunting; by gathering wild fruits, nuts and honey; by fishing with woven baskets; and by cultivating small gardens. When the soil is depleted, they move on. Usually, the men hunt and fish while the women tend crops. Children assist the adults and learn how to thrive in their environment, as almost all of the food, clothing, and medicines for the tribes come from jungle resources. The **onus** for passing down knowledge of the jungle's medicinal assets rests with medicine men. As long as isolated tribes have access to natural resources and territory, they have told researchers they "live well," according to a 2007 study by Amazon Today. Many of these tribes made deliberate decisions to remain apart from outsiders after the so-called rubber boom, during which indigenous people were exploited for their land and labor for rubber plantations. Although Western demand meant a **profligate** lifestyle for some Europeans who owned plantations, the owners failed to **remit** profits to local tribes.

Contact, whether **impromptu** or carefully planned, comes with problems, particularly disease. Many indigenous peoples lack the **requisite** immunities to diseases brought in from the outside world. During the past 100 years, from the time records were kept, 50 percent of a tribe's members died within a year of contact. Today, Brazilian officials say they have long known of so-called uncontacted or isolated tribes in the area where the latest tribe was photographed. When outsiders leave metal pots, tools, and machetes behind in areas frequented by these tribes, the indigenous people take the objects, often without revealing themselves. Since the late 1980s, out of **deference** to their way of life, Brazilian officials have monitored the tribes and **curtailed** efforts to contact them. This policy **mollified** an international **brouhaha** over the tribes' dismal survival rates after contact.

A road winds through a logged area in the Brazilian rain forest.

Snap the code, or go to
vocabularyworkshop.com

Definitions

Note the spelling, pronunciation, part(s) of speech, and definition(s) of each of the following words. Then write the word in the blank spaces in the illustrative sentence(s) following. Finally, study the lists of synonyms and antonyms.

1. adamant
(ad' ə mənt)

(*adj.*) firm in purpose or opinion, unyielding, obdurate, implacable, inflexible; (*n.*) an extremely hard substance

The government was _____ in its refusal to negotiate with terrorists.

When writers referred to _____ centuries ago, they sometimes meant diamonds or magnetized iron.

ANTONYMS: (*adj.*) yielding, flexible, pliable

2. brouhaha
(brü' hä hä)

(*n.*) a confused hodgepodge of sounds, hubbub; an uproar or commotion that goes far beyond what is justified

After the _____ had finally subsided, we asked the group to give us a written list of all their complaints.

SYNONYMS: hullabaloo, tumult, pandemonium

3. bulwark
(bəl' wərk)

(*n.*) a strong defense or protection, a solid wall-like structure for defense; (*v.*) to provide such defense or protection

The only evidence of a once thriving civilization is this _____ against the ocean tides.

The singer's staff had to _____ him against fans who wanted to get near him.

SYNONYMS: (*n.*) bastion, rampart; ANTONYM: (*n.*) breach

4. choleric
(käl' ər ik)

(*adj.*) easily made angry, bad-tempered

His _____ temperament and erratic behavior made him an ineffective ruler.

SYNONYMS: irascible, testy, splenetic, bilious
ANTONYMS: affable, genial, even-tempered

5. cloy
(kloi)

(*v.*) to spoil or destroy an appetite by too much indulgence, especially in sweet or rich things; to glut, satiate, surfeit

A steady diet of TV began to _____, and I was glad to begin a book.

ANTONYMS: stimulate, whet

6. curtail
(kər tāl')

(*v.*) to cut short, bring to a halt, or end sooner than expected; to reduce

It is time yet again to _____ the flow of unsolicited nonsense that somehow reaches me as e-mail.

SYNONYMS: limit, abbreviate, abridge, contract
ANTONYMS: protract, extend

7. deference
(def′ ər əns)

(*n.*) courteous yielding to the wishes and ideas of another person; great respect marked by submission, as to a superior

Some moderate _____ is due the boss, but too much can seem to conceal other motives.

SYNONYMS: respect, consideration; ANTONYMS: contempt, disdain

8. definitive
(də fin′ ə tiv)

(*adj.*) conclusive, final, the limit of what can be done

She is working on what she hopes will be the _____ biography of Emily Dickinson.

SYNONYMS: exhaustive, authoritative; ANTONYM: tentative

9. demeanor
(di mē′ nər)

(*n.*) the way a person behaves, overall impression made by comportment, manner, etc.; facial appearance, mien

Charles Dickens's Mr. Pickwick has such a cheerful and sympathetic _____ that few can resist him.

SYNONYMS: conduct, behavior, carriage

10. enigmatic
(en ig mat′ ik)

(*adj.*) puzzling, perplexing, inexplicable, not easily understood

He was staring me straight in the eye, neither pleased nor displeased, his expression _____.

SYNONYMS: baffling, mysterious, inexplicable
ANTONYMS: intelligible, understandable, fathomable

11. impromptu
(im prämp′ tü)

(*adj., adv.*) without preparation, offhand, suddenly or hastily done; (*n.*) an extemporaneous composition or remark; a minimal piece suggestive of improvisation

His _____ speech allowed him to express not only what he was thinking but also what he was feeling.

An _____ by Schubert may not stun you at first, but you'll find hours later that you haven't forgotten it.

SYNONYMS: (*adj.*) spontaneous, improvised, unrehearsed
ANTONYMS: (*adj.*) rehearsed, planned, premeditated

12. mawkish
(mô′ kish)

(*adj.*) excessively and objectionably sentimental; having a mildly sickening flavor

Jimmy Stewart's portrayal of his character in *It's a Wonderful Life was* poignant without being _____.

SYNONYMS: sentimentalized, mushy, nauseating
ANTONYMS: unsentimental, callous, insensitive

13. mollify
(mäl′ ə fī)

(*v.*) to soften; to calm, allay (as an emotion); reduce in intensity

The senator hoped to _____ her angry public, but nothing she said was likely to get her reelected.

SYNONYMS: pacify, placate; ANTONYMS: aggravate, exacerbate

14. onus
(ō′ nəs)

(*n.*) something that is heavy or burdensome (especially an unwelcome responsibility); a stigma; blame

If the _____ for a defective product is placed on the consumer, some complicated legal and ethical questions are sure to arise.

SYNONYMS: obligation, duty

15. presentiment
(pre zen′ tə ment)

(*n.*) a vague sense of approaching misfortune

Ironically, by denying their _____, they made their worst fears come true.

SYNONYMS: foreboding, premonition, hunch

16. profligate
(präf′ lə gət)

(*adj.*) given over to dissipation and self-indulgence, immoral; recklessly extravagant; (*n.*) a person given to wild spending

He was the family's _____ son, the charming one from whom nothing was expected.

She was a _____, and no matter how much money she earned, she always spent more than she had.

SYNONYMS: (*adj.*) prodigal, improvident; (*n.*) spendthrift
ANTONYMS: (*adj.*) penny-pinching, frugal, economical

17. remit
(ri mit′)

(*v.*) to send or hand in (as money); to cancel (as a penalty or punishment), forgive; to lessen, diminish; postpone, defer

They would _____ a certain sum each year to a local charity.

SYNONYMS: absolve, subside, abate, pardon

18. requisite
(rek′ wə zit)

(*adj.*) needed, necessary, regarded as essential or indispensable

If you have the _____ coordination and an ear for music, I'll pay for your first year of dance instruction.

SYNONYMS: required, obligatory, incumbent
ANTONYMS: nonessential, superfluous, optional

19. sartorial
(sär tôr′ ē əl)

(*adj.*) of or pertaining to a tailor or his work; having to do with clothes or dress (especially men's)

Paging through historical picture books is a fascinating study in _____ standards through the centuries.

20. thwart
(thwôrt)

(*v.*) to oppose successfully; to prevent, frustrate

Our dog's friendliness would _____ the sternest efforts of the most expensive guard-dog trainer.

SYNONYMS: foil, baffle
ANTONYMS: aid, assist, abet, further

Choosing the Right Word

*Select the **boldface** word that better completes each sentence. You might refer to the selection on pages 184–185 to see how most of these words are used in context.*

1. I am a great admirer of Charles Dickens, but even I must admit that the death of Little Nell in *The Old Curiosity Shop* is too (**sartorial, mawkish**) to be truly effective.

2. The scientific method stands as a(n) (**bulwark, onus**) against the tides of irrationality and superstition.

3. His constant blustering and (**definitive, choleric**) behavior may be no more than an unconscious attempt to conceal his lack of self-confidence.

4. I am surprised that she now shows such exaggerated (**deference, adamant**) to people whose "aristocratic" pretensions she has always regarded with contempt.

5. After years of (**profligate, enigmatic**) living, he experienced a profound change of heart and devoted the rest of his life to serving humanity.

Many of Dickens's novels, including *The Old Curiosity Shop*, were originally published as weekly serials.

6. Her bitter anger was eventually (**mollified, thwarted**) by our skillful appeals to her vanity.

7. Let us place the (**presentiment, onus**) for the defeat where it belongs—on each and every one of us!

8. Our coach is (**adamant, mawkish**) that we not drink sugary sports drinks before a game and insists that we hydrate only with water.

9. When you have a feeling that something is about to happen, you may unconsciously act in a way that will help the (**brouhaha, presentiment**) to come true.

10. Though my sister has many close friends, she is a(n) (**bulwark, enigma**) who is reluctant to share her private thoughts and feelings.

11. His aggressive and suspicious (**deference, demeanor**) led the detectives to suspect that he was more involved with the crime than he alleged.

12. Scholastic proficiency, emotional stability, and a genuine interest in young people are (**profligate, requisite**) qualities for a good teacher.

13. After tallying the bills and invoices, the young newlyweds began the odious task of (**remitting, mollifying**) payments to the wedding planner, florist, and photographer.

14. Far from being (**impromptu, profligate**), all those jokes and wisecracks you hear on TV talk shows are usually prepared by professional writers and are carefully rehearsed.

15. When we received bad news from home, we had to (**remit, curtail**) our vacation and return a few days earlier than planned.

16. Their efforts to win the game by a last-minute trick play were (**thwarted, remitted**) when our alert safety intercepted the deep pass.

17. The special privileges extended to the senior class have not been entirely withdrawn, but they have been sharply (**thwarted, curtailed**) for the rest of the term.

18. Her unvarying sweetness, like a diet composed entirely of desserts, does begin to (**cloy, mollify**) after a while.

19. Expressing his mystification at the Soviet Union, Churchill referred to it as a "riddle wrapped in a mystery inside an (**enigma, onus**)."

20. We all admired her (**demeanor, presentiment**), which was dignified without any suggestion of superiority or stuffiness.

21. The recent (**presentiment, brouhaha**) over the choice of a host for our local beauty pageant seemed to me nothing more than a "tempest in a teapot."

22. He delivered his speech poorly, but since he was the best-dressed man on the dais that afternoon, he enjoyed a (**sartorial, profligate**) if not an oratorical triumph.

23. I came to realize that the demure little woman who never raised her voice had a will of pure (**adamant, deference**).

24. There are so many aspects to Shakespeare that there will never be a truly (**definitive, impromptu**) study of his work.

25. You can't enroll in this advanced class without the (**requisite, definitive**) courses.

 **Synonyms**

*Choose the word from this unit that is the same or most nearly the same in meaning as the **boldface** word or expression in the phrase. Write that word on the line. Use a dictionary if necessary.*

1. a clearly expressed yet **mystifying** statement _____

2. a solemn and mournful **bearing** _____

3. a heavy **burden** to bear _____

4. would **pay** the fine _____

5. received an **omen** _____

6. **obstruct** a complicated plot _____

7. a **maudlin** love story _____

8. his **crotchety** reaction to any interruption _____

9. felt protected inside the **fortress** _____

10. sweet snacks **slaked** her appetite for dinner _____

Antonyms

*Choose the word from this unit that is most nearly opposite in meaning to the **boldface** word or expression in the phrase. Write that word on the line. Use a dictionary if necessary.*

1. an **unsympathetic** response to her tale of woe _____

2. show **scorn** for the leader _____

3. a **prepared** statement for the press _____

4. **foment** an interest in golf _____

5. an **amiable** reply to the question _____

Completing the Sentence

From the words in this unit, choose the one that best completes each of the following sentences. Write the word in the space provided.

1. I think that the phrase "having a short fuse" aptly describes my new boss's _____ and curmudgeonly disposition.

2. We heard that the South High fans were planning to "kidnap" our mascot before the game, and we were determined to _____ them.

3. In his black jacket, light gray slacks, and tailored sport shirt, he was a model of _____ elegance.

4. Somehow, whenever more money is needed for our club activities, the _____ of raising it always seems to fall on me.

5. The candidate seems much more human and appealing when she delivers a(n) _____ speech than when she reads a prepared text.

6. Throughout the trial she maintained a(n) _____ of quiet dignity and confidence that made a favorable impression on the jury.

7. In _____ to the wishes of the widow, the funeral services will be brief, and no eulogy will be delivered.

8. When the chairperson saw that the speakers were becoming more heated, without offering any new facts or ideas to clarify the situation, she decided to _____ the discussion period.

9. Although we must have armed forces to protect the country, the most important _____ of national security is the devotion of the people to our democratic institutions.

10. How can you watch those silly reruns of old family shows day after day without being _____ by their gooey sentimentality?

11. I was surprised that so trivial an incident should have provided such a fearful _____ in the popular press.

12. We are still looking for a(n) _____ answer to the question of whether or not our prisons can rehabilitate as well as punish.

13. I see no point in your applying for that job when it is perfectly clear that you lack the _____ qualifications.

14. The circumstances surrounding the death are so _____ that the police are not even sure that a crime was committed.

15. Attached to every bill for the merchandise was a brief notice asking the customer to _____ payment promptly.

16. By talking so much about your _____ that "we're going to have an accident," you are making me nervous and preventing me from driving properly.

17. By getting the students to apologize for their thoughtless discourtesy, we _____ the anger of the elderly elevator operator.

18. He was willing to compromise on many issues, but elimination of the ridiculous requirements for those jobs was the one point on which he was absolutely

_____ .

19. He was so _____ with his inheritance that he consumed in a few years the fortune it had taken his parents a lifetime to accumulate.

20. At first, I was glad to see my old classmate again, but he embarrassed me with his _____ talk about "those wonderful, golden school days."

Writing: Words in Action

1. Look back at "New Tribe Discovered in Amazon" (pages 184–185). Suppose you were hired to persuade Brazilian officials and others that we should not interfere with the way of life of indigenous peoples in the Amazon. Write your argument using at least two details from the passage and three unit words.

2. What, if anything, do you think citizens or governments should do to protect indigenous peoples? What responsibility do nations have to respect indigenous people's way of life and protect the areas where they live? In a brief essay, support your opinion with specific details from your observations, studies, and the reading (pages 184–185). Write at least three paragraphs, and use three or more words from this unit.

Vocabulary in Context

Literary Text

The following excerpts are from Tales of a Traveller *by Washington Irving. Some of the words you have studied in this unit appear in* **boldface** *type. Complete each statement below the excerpt by circling the letter of the correct answer.*

1. To see him on Sunday, so stiff and starched in his **demeanor**; so precise in his dress; with his daughter under his arm, and his ivory-headed cane in his hand, was enough to deter all graceless youngsters from approaching.

   A person's **demeanor** is his or her
   a. viewpoint   **c.** upbringing
   b. manner   **d.** profession

2. A deep sleep had already fallen upon this primitive little burgh; nothing disturbed this awful silence, excepting now and then the bark of some **profligate** night-walking dog, or the serenade of some romantic cat.

   A **profligate** dog is NOT
   a. unrestrained   **c.** wild
   b. irresponsible **d.** cautious

3. He would now have entered into a full detail, but was **thwarted** by the Englishman, who seemed determined not to credit or indulge him in his stories.

   If a storyteller is **thwarted**, he or she is
   a. changed   **c.** discouraged
   b. exaggerated   **d.** abetted

Often called "the father of the American short story," Washington Irving was the first American author to make a living from his writing.

4. There was a story also of a gentleman of Rome, who delayed **remitting** the ransom demanded for his son, detained by the banditti, and received one of his son's ears in a letter with information that the other would be remitted to him soon, if the money were not forthcoming, and that in this way he would receive the boy by installments until he came to terms.

   The act of **remitting** involves
   a. paying   **c.** obtaining
   b. distracting   **d.** producing

5. The faintly lighted apartment had all the qualifications **requisite** for a haunted chamber. It began in my infected imagination to assume strange appearances. The old portraits turned paler and paler, and blacker and blacker; the streaks of light and shadow thrown among the quaint old articles of furniture, gave them singular shapes....

   Qualifications that are **requisite** are
   a. pleasurable   **c.** unexpected
   b. compulsory   **d.** terrifying

Interactive Quiz

Snap the code, or go to **vocabularyworkshop.com**

Vocabulary for Comprehension

*Read the following selection in which some of the words you have studied in Units 13–15 appear in **boldface** type. Then answer the questions on page 195.*

This passage discusses the long, colorful history of American political campaigns.

(Line)

Before the birth of the modern media, staging a campaign to elect an American President was a scattered, street-level affair.

(5) Professional pollsters, convention planners, and spin doctors did not yet exist, and the task of drawing attention to a candidate's name and platform was relegated to party

(10) members and neighborhood volunteers.

The very idea of campaigning would have **nonplussed** the first presidential candidate. George

(15) Washington, running without an opponent, was unanimously elected President. He served two terms in office purely out of a sense of duty. Having led an amateur army to

(20) defeat the British Empire, this tall, **impassive**, and dignified hero seemed, by any **criterion**, a national leader beyond compare.

But when the right to vote was

(25) extended, political parties formed. These parties needed to publicize their ideas in order to stir up party sentiment and attract new members. Colorful banners were unfurled in

(30) public places, blazoning a candidate's virtues and ideology. Citizens were encouraged to announce their party loyalty by

wearing it where one could see

(35) it—on cheap badges hung from around the neck or else from printed ribbons hung from a pin. (Campaign buttons with pins on the back, still produced today, did not appear until

(40) 1896.) All such attention-getters (they included printed bandanas) bore the candidate's name or nickname—and a slogan if there was room. Slogans were hugely popular.

(45) Campaigners for William Henry Harrison rolled enormous metal spheres, painted with slogans, through city streets.

From Andrew Jackson's second

(50) campaign onward, rowdy picnics, barbecues, and loud parades were used to attract the voters, much as they are used in primary-election campaigns today. Even Abraham

(55) Lincoln had his carnival-like supporters who contributed to the general **brouhaha**; the Wide-Awakes, as they called themselves (awake to **thwart** the enemy,

(60) slavery), marched in closely drilled formations, sporting shiny hats and capes.

In addition, countless speeches were made and handbills printed.

(65) But first and last the message was simply: "Look here, look here!"

1. The primary purpose of the first paragraph (lines 1–11) is to
   a. draw attention to the writer's expertise
   b. highlight the distortions introduced by spin doctors
   c. ridicule old-style campaigns
   d. refute the notion that campaigns are overly scripted and predictable
   e. compare and contrast campaigns before and after the birth of the modern media

2. According to the passage, who handled old-style political campaigns?
   a. sloganeers
   b. professional pollsters
   c. party members and neighborhood volunteers
   d. the candidates themselves
   e. convention planners

3. The meaning of **nonplussed** (line 13) is
   a. bored
   b. excited
   c. outraged
   d. amused
   e. perplexed

4. **Impassive** (line 21) most nearly means
   a. stoical
   b. hard-working
   c. charismatic
   d. conceited
   e. proud

5. **Criterion** (line 22) is best defined as
   a. vote
   b. alias
   c. name
   d. yardstick
   e. opinion

6. The writer discusses Washington in paragraph 2 (lines 12–23) primarily to
   a. compare Washington with Lincoln
   b. emphasize Washington's ambition
   c. give the reader a sense of Washington's personality
   d. show that Washington's election was unlike today's election campaigns
   e. credit Washington with designing the first organized political campaign

7. From paragraph 3 (lines 24–48), you can infer that which of the following was a watershed event in the transformation of political campaigns?
   a. westward expansion
   b. the formation of political parties
   c. the invention of campaign buttons
   d. the increasing ingenuity of slogans
   e. the presidential campaign of William Henry Harrison

8. According to the passage, how did the "Wide-Awakes" get their name?
   a. They were highly intelligent.
   b. They were "wide awake" against slavery.
   c. They marched wearing shiny hats and capes.
   d. They campaigned day and night.
   e. They carefully examined the records of opposing candidates.

9. **Brouhaha** (line 57) most nearly means
   a. fear
   b. cheerfulness
   c. anger
   d. confusion
   e. hullabaloo

10. **Thwart** (line 59) is best defined as
    a. foil
    b. reform
    c. analyze
    d. capture
    e. debate

11. The author's attitude is mainly
    a. quizzical
    b. sarcastic
    c. animated
    d. indifferent
    e. charitable

12. The quoted words "Look here, look here!" in the last paragraph (lines 63–65) convey an election's
    a. indecision
    b. patience
    c. excitement
    d. seriousness
    e. importance

Two-Word Completions

Select the pair of words that best complete the meaning of each of the following passages.

1. Once our fossil-fuel reserves are exhausted, they are gone forever. For that reason, we should try to _____ our use of these precious resources so that they are not _____ too quickly.
   - **a.** abet . . . nonplussed
   - **b.** curtail . . . depleted
   - **c.** remit . . . expatiated
   - **d.** mollify . . . buttressed

2. Mozart was a(n) _____ youngster who wrote his first opera at the age of eleven. Though he was never as _____ a composer of theater music as some of his contemporaries, his output of stage works was by no means negligible.
   - **a.** precocious . . . prolific
   - **b.** sententious . . . incontrovertible
   - **c.** credulous . . . profligate
   - **d.** enigmatic . . . blatant

3. No matter how much protective consumer legislation we pass in order to _____ would-be swindlers and con artists, there probably will always be _____ people around for them to prey on.
   - **a.** buttress . . . adamant
   - **b.** thwart . . . credulous
   - **c.** abet . . . jejune
   - **d.** curtail . . . precocious

4. Friends hoped that the tearful _____ of the mother would soften the king's heart toward the young reprobates, but the dour old man _____ refused to yield to her entreaties.
   - **a.** presentiments . . . obdurately
   - **b.** demeanor . . . mawkishly
   - **c.** supplications . . . adamantly
   - **d.** deference . . . disconsolately

5. During the battle, the _____ had been horrendous. Where the fighting had been the fiercest, the bodies were piled three deep. It took days to complete the _____ task of burying the dead.
   - **a.** surfeit . . . turgid
   - **b.** brouhaha . . . herculean
   - **c.** carnage . . . grisly
   - **d.** onus . . . mawkish

6. Though one of his parents reacted to the unexpected news of his death with a(n) _____ display of emotion, the other received it with all the _____ restraint of a true stoic.
   - **a.** enigmatic . . . credulous
   - **b.** mawkish . . . choleric
   - **c.** sadistic . . . deferential
   - **d.** blatant . . . impassive

7. His start in life had been _____, but with hard work and a good deal of luck, he became a widely respected _____ of fine antique furniture and rare books.
   - **a.** inauspicious . . . connoisseur
   - **b.** tortuous . . . bulwark
   - **c.** profligate . . . criterion
   - **d.** sartorial . . . rejoinder

Idioms

In the essay "Ansel Adams" (see pages 164–165), the author states that Adams barely "kept his head above water" when he was in school. Of course, Adams was not literally drowning; the saying is an idiom that means "managing to survive in a difficult situation."

Idioms are short, witty expressions that should be interpreted figuratively. You often can only grasp their meanings in context. Although idioms can add color and verve to writing, they should be used sparingly. When idioms are overused, they become clichés—expressions so commonplace that they have become stale and meaningless.

Choosing the Right Idiom

Read each sentence. Use context clues to figure out the meaning of each idiom in **boldface** *print. Then write the letter of the definition for the idiom in the sentence.*

1. When someone stole her secret formula for a new lotion, and all her research **went down the drain**, Claire was furious. _____

2. I have to **hand it to you**, Doug: Your speech motivated everyone to participate in the savings program. _____

3. Jack decided to **bury the hatchet** with his brother and attend his birthday party. _____

4. I would **give my right arm** to be able to get a job working at a radio station. _____

5. Well, I sure had fun vacationing at the beach, but it's **back to the salt mines** when I get home. _____

6. My parents told me that if I **play my cards right**, they will help me buy a car. _____

7. Tori, who **had her heart set on** seeing the Broadway show, cried when the tickets were sold out. _____

8. Jon was **on cloud nine** when he learned he had just been awarded a full scholarship. _____

9. His name **rings a bell**, but I'm not sure I can remember what movie he is in. _____

10. I hate to **split hairs** with you, but the trip took fifty-five minutes, not an hour. _____

a. return to the routine of work

b. be willing to sacrifice something of great value

c. argue about insignificant details

d. do the correct thing to achieve a desired result

e. wanted to do something very much; desired deeply

f. was wasted, lost, or destroyed

g. sounds familiar

h. in an ecstatic state

i. give credit or acknowledgment

j. end a fight or make peace

Writing with Idioms

Find the meaning of each idiom. (Use an online or print dictionary if necessary.) Then write a sentence for each idiom.

1. save your breath

_____

2. all in your head

_____

3. go against the grain

_____

4. call it off

_____

5. string someone along

_____

_____

6. hang out to dry

_____

_____

7. have a bone to pick

_____

_____

8. cut and dried

_____

9. get over it

_____

10. off the hook

_____

11. recipe for disaster

_____

12. up for grabs

_____

Denotation and Connotation

A dictionary entry tells you a word's literal meaning, or **denotation**. Yet a word's synonyms, which have similar denotations, carry different shades of meaning based on the associations we make to them. We call these associations **connotations**.

A word's connotations may be positive or negative. One writer may describe a star athlete as *aggressive*, a word with negative connotations. Another writer may describe the same athlete as *assertive*, a word with positive connotations. Because they have such different connotations, few synonyms are completely interchangeable.

Consider these synonyms for the word *foment*:

> stimulate   encourage   provoke   incite

Stimulate and *encourage* have positive connotations, whereas *provoke* and *incite* have more negative connotations.

> **Think:** A peaceful reformer hopes to *stimulate* and *encourage* people to make social changes, but a violent rebel tries to *provoke* or *incite* civil unrest.

Look at these examples of words that are similar in denotation but have different connotations.

NEUTRAL	POSITIVE	NEGATIVE
abet	encourage	goad
clear	evident	blatant
calm	mollify	appease

A writer's use of connotative words provides clues about his or her purpose and point of view. As you read, ask yourself why certain words stir up strong emotions, and think about why the writer might have used those specific words.

Shades of Meaning

Write a plus sign (+) in the box if the word has a positive connotation.
Write a minus sign (–) if the word has a negative connotation. Put a zero (0)
if the word is neutral.

1. choleric ☐   **2.** herculean ☐   **3.** berate ☐   **4.** thwart ☐

5. encumber ☐   **6.** turgid ☐   **7.** collate ☐   **8.** prolific ☐

9. connoisseur ☐   **10.** carnage ☐   **11.** precocious ☐   **12.** sadistic ☐

13. criterion ☐   **14.** broach ☐   **15.** grisly ☐   **16.** amenable ☐

WORD STUDY

Expressing the Connotation

Read each sentence. Select the word in parentheses that expresses the connotation (positive, negative, or neutral) given at the beginning of the sentence.

neutral
1. Completing this math problem requires several (**tortuous, complex**) steps.

positive
2. Nadia wrote a (**mawkish, touching**) poem about her grandparents.

positive
3. My music collection is a (**potpourri, hodgepodge**) of various genres, from country to classical.

positive
4. There will be a huge (**responsibility, onus**) on you should you decide to take on that project.

negative
5. Your (**inauspicious, unpromising**) plan to take a drive during a tornado was not greeted with enthusiasm.

negative
6. The (**riot, brouhaha**) began when the officials refused to let participants enter the stadium early.

positive
7. My sister, a university professor, is writing a (**reliable, definitive**) reference work about the origins of common idioms.

negative
8. I will not let the necessity of holding a day job (**thwart, affect**) my objective of finishing night school.

Challenge: Using Connotation

Choose vocabulary words from Units 13–15 to replace the highlighted words in the sentences below. Then explain how the connotation of the replacement word changes the tone of the sentence.

demeanor	jejune	infirmity
curtail	nonplussed	abet

1. When Shawna told me that my clothes were hideous and out of style, I was **flabbergasted** _____.

_____

_____

2. The cause of my uncle's **defect** _____ was a mystery to the doctors, even after they ran several tests.

_____

_____

3. I read that if you drink a glass of water before a meal, it will **restrict** _____ your desire to eat a huge meal.

_____

_____

Classical Roots

quer, ques, quis—to seek, ask

The root *quis* appears in **requisite** (page 188), which means "essential, necessary." Some other words based on related roots are listed below.

disquisition	inquisition	perquisite	query
inquest	inquisitive	prerequisite	requisition

From the list of words above, choose the one that corresponds to each of the brief definitions below. Write the word in the blank space in the illustrative sentence below the definition. Use an online or print dictionary if necessary.

1. a legal inquiry before a jury (*"asking into"*)

The family of the victim attended the coroner's _____.

2. a long and formal speech or writing about a subject

The scientist prepared a scholarly _____ on her findings.

3. eager for knowledge; given to inquiry or research, curious; nosy, prying

A good detective needs a(n) _____ mind.

4. to ask, ask about, inquire into; to express doubts about; a question or inquiry

If you have a question about that newspaper article, _____ the editor.

5. a severe investigation; an official inquiry conducted with little regard for human rights

The zealous reporter turned a simple interview into a(n) _____.

6. a demand or application made in an authoritative way; to demand or call for with authority

The department made a(n) _____ for ten additional trucks.

7. an extra payment; anything received for work besides regular compensation (*"that which is sought"*)

She enjoyed the _____ of her office.

8. that which is necessary beforehand; a qualification (*as for enrolling in a course*)

Beginning Spanish is a(n) _____ for advanced Spanish.

Synonyms

Select the two words or expressions that are most nearly the same in meaning.

1. **a.** foment   **b.** cause   **c.** repress   **d.** elicit

2. **a.** deleterious   **b.** gauche   **c.** graceless   **d.** clever

3. **a.** enthrall   **b.** horrify   **c.** charm   **d.** prate

4. **a.** onus   **b.** approbation   **c.** approval   **d.** indifference

5. **a.** scintillating   **b.** choleric   **c.** discordant   **d.** witty

6. **a.** hiatus   **b.** disagreement   **c.** pause   **d.** coalition

7. **a.** recognition   **b.** autonomy   **c.** decadence   **d.** independence

8. **a.** lassitude   **b.** clangor   **c.** eagerness   **d.** weariness

9. **a.** enthusiastic   **b.** motley   **c.** diverse   **d.** dowdy

10. **a.** disabuse   **b.** learn   **c.** recapitulate   **d.** summarize

11. **a.** saturate   **b.** scour   **c.** permeate   **d.** foist

12. **a.** grandiose   **b.** profitable   **c.** extravagant   **d.** punctilious

13. **a.** cowardice   **b.** perfidy   **c.** amnesty   **d.** treachery

14. **a.** sanctimonious   **b.** hypocritical   **c.** spontaneous   **d.** evanescent

15. **a.** gratuitous   **b.** unstated   **c.** implicit   **d.** overt

Antonyms

Select the two words that are most nearly opposite in meaning.

16. **a.** impassive   **b.** imperious   **c.** remarkable   **d.** subservient

17. **a.** hackneyed   **b.** provincial   **c.** novel   **d.** insular

18. **a.** infirmity   **b.** sadistic   **c.** decisive   **d.** humane

19. **a.** dissension   **b.** gossamer   **c.** simple   **d.** agreement

20. **a.** fractious   **b.** dilatory   **c.** expensive   **d.** prompt

21. **a.** enigmatic   **b.** deliberate   **c.** inadvertent   **d.** harsh

22. **a.** produce   **b.** aver   **c.** disavow   **d.** supplicate

23. **a.** politic   **b.** imprudent   **c.** abundant   **d.** resilient

24. **a.** grisly   **b.** torpid   **c.** energetic   **d.** intellectual

25. **a.** collate   **b.** extricate   **c.** embroil   **d.** rearrange

Analogies

Select the item that best completes the comparison.

26. deft is to **aplomb** as
- a. vitriolic is to tact
- b. nonchalant is to sangfroid
- c. unctuous is to wisdom
- d. seditious is to persistence

27. millennium is to **year** as
- a. quart is to pint
- b. mile is to foot
- c. kilo is to gram
- d. meter is to yard

28. circuitous is to **twists** as
- a. sinuous is to gaps
- b. serrated is to knots
- c. gnarled is to curves
- d. jagged is to irregularities

29. transient is to **pass through** as
- a. itinerant is to occupy
- b. pioneer is to settle
- c. resident is to visit
- d. tourist is to colonize

30. inscrutable is to **decipher** as
- a. invisible is to overlook
- b. immutable is to persist
- c. irrevocable is to retract
- d. innocuous is to harm

31. crypt is to **sepulchral** as
- a. mansion is to penurious
- b. palace is to indigent
- c. prison is to soporific
- d. slum is to squalid

32. grisly is to **horror** as
- a. jejune is to interest
- b. revolting is to disgust
- c. appalling is to joy
- d. ominous is to exultation

33. corpulent is to **obese** as
- a. nebulous is to lucid
- b. succinct is to terse
- c. slovenly is to untidy
- d. skinny is to cadaverous

Two-Word Completions

Select the best word pair from among the choices given.

34. The _____ manner of the hostess, who greeted us with warmth, left us unprepared for the _____ behavior of the wait staff.
- a. adamant . . . bovine
- b. bizarre . . . culpable
- c. affable . . . brusque
- d. crass . . . meritorious

35. To our disappointment and _____, the author made a host of _____ demands in return for appearing at the book fair.
- a. adulation . . . beneficent
- b. odium . . . jejune
- c. penury . . . insurgent
- d. consternation . . . petulant

36. Rather than _____, the response of the boisterous crowd in the theater grew more and more _____.
- a. abate . . . bombastic
- b. abominate . . . anomalous
- c. ferment . . . ignoble
- d. infringe . . . heinous

37. My dog knows she can _____ treats from me because I am _____ to her sad, imploring eyes.
- a. wheedle . . . susceptible
- b. remonstrate . . . surreptitious
- c. exhort . . . unwieldy
- d. transcend . . . jaded

Supplying Words in Context

To complete each sentence, select the best word from among the choices given. Not all words in the word bank will be used. You may modify the word form as necessary.

debase	amnesty	equitable	contraband
ingratiate	nominal	decadence	austere
fetter	coalition	mitigate	elicit
axiomatic	erudite	anathema	anomalous

38. If people pay their overdue fines by the end of the month, they will be given _____ regarding late fees.

39. In an effort to _____ himself, he offered to do all of the chores.

40. Speaking in such a disrespectful way would have been _____ to my grandparents.

41. In order to tackle so difficult an issue, I recommend we seek to form a _____ of interested groups that will work together.

42. The police dogs are specially trained to be able to detect _____.

43. Both sides involved in the recent controversy were pleased by the _____ nature of the settlement.

propensity	flout	impugn	castigate
assuage	sedulous	desecrate	enjoin
surmise	filch	acculturation	aspersion
astute	proclivity	vicarious	novice

44. To _____ the rules in such an obvious manner could not help but draw attention.

45. The process of _____ may involve a complete immersion in the new language and habits of living.

46. Your _____ observation indicates a great deal of experience in this academic field.

47. As I had been warned repeatedly, for the teacher to _____ me was completely understandable.

48. For a(n) _____ at the sport, she performed extremely well.

49. Speaking soothingly, my father sought to _____ my sorrowful feelings when my best friend moved to Europe.

Word Associations

*Select the word or expression that best completes the meaning of the sentence or answers the question, with particular reference to the meaning of the word in **boldface** type.*

50. The distinguishing symptom of a person suffering from **megalomania** is
  a. chronic depression
  b. high blood pressure
  c. delusions of grandeur
  d. problem dandruff

51. Taking **umbrage** would be a reasonable reaction when you are
  a. complimented
  b. insulted
  c. rewarded
  d. introduced to someone new

52. Which of the following is the best remedy for being **callow**?
  a. time and experience
  b. dancing lessons
  c. vitamins
  d. sun and surf

53. Which of the following reactions would best characterize someone suffering from **ennui**?
  a. a smile
  b. a wink
  c. a yawn
  d. a grimace

54. A person who is the **epitome** of wit
  a. uses it maliciously
  b. is actually not very witty
  c. is an ideal example of wittiness
  d. employs wit in a strange way

55. Which of the following would by definition be guilty of **peculation**?
  a. a judge
  b. a coward
  c. an embezzler
  d. a philanthropist

56. If you receive a **noncommittal** reply to a request, you will probably be
  a. in a state of uncertainty
  b. deeply depressed
  c. overjoyed
  d. ready to fight

57. To describe an author as **prolific** refers to
  a. nationality
  b. the size of the author's bank account
  c. relations with critics
  d. the number of books produced

58. The usual reason for **expurgating** a book is to
  a. get rid of objectionable material
  b. make it more readable
  c. translate it into a foreign language
  d. reissue it as an e-book

59. A person who has suffered an **egregious** defeat has lost
  a. gloriously
  b. conspicuously
  c. by a close score
  d. as a result of unfair tactics

60. You would **buttress** an argument if you wanted to
  a. incite it
  b. support it
  c. avoid it
  d. repudiate it

61. Good advice to someone who is constantly being **dunned** is
  a. Go home!
  b. Keep your eye on the ball!
  c. Don't waste fuel!
  d. Pay your bills!

Choosing the Right Meaning

Read each sentence carefully. Then select the item that best completes the statement below the sentence.

62. The **acrimonious** nature of our first encounter has made our relationship extremely difficult ever since.

The word **acrimonious** most nearly means

a. hostile **b.** herculean **c.** magnanimous **d.** weird

63. Our school principal projected such an **aura** of competence that no one questioned her ability to make the right decisions on behalf of the school.

The word **aura** most nearly means

a. atmosphere **b.** cause **c.** fear **d.** expectation

64. The children's reaction to the strange man's behavior only served to further **disconcert** the other people in the park.

The word **disconcert** most nearly means

a. praise **b.** replace **c.** upset **d.** aggrandize

65. The administrator said he would **expedite** our application so we would not have to spend the afternoon waiting for the results.

The word **expedite** most nearly means

a. augment **b.** berate **c.** delay **d.** facilitate

66. The author's wise **precepts** laid out a philosophy of life that it would be fruitful to use as a model.

The word **precepts** most nearly means

a. caveats **b.** infractions **c.** principles **d.** innuendos

67. The polar expedition's exploits have been **blazoned** on the pages of history, inspiring generations of geographers and adventurers.

The best definition for the word **blazoned** is

a. cajoled **b.** displayed **c.** ignored **d.** absolved

68. The planners recognize the need to **transmute** the economic system from an industrial base to a concentration on providing services.

The word **transmute** most nearly means

a. converge **b.** accrue **c.** change **d.** inveigh

69. Nothing in the politician's record could lead anyone to **ascribe** to him such outlandish views.

The word **ascribe** most nearly means

a. revive **b.** attribute **c.** expiate **d.** reverberate

70. Taking the medication for the full course prescribed will serve best to **ameliorate** the condition.

The word **ameliorate** is best defined as

a. disavow **b.** lament **c.** improve **d.** contrive

WORD LIST

The following is a list of all the words taught in the Units of this book. The number after each entry indicates the page on which the word is defined.

abate, 110
abet, 166
abominate, 34
absolve, 148
abstemious, 138
accrue, 128
acculturation, 34
acrimonious, 100
adamant, 186
adulation, 110
adventitious, 34
affable, 52
aggrandize, 52
ameliorate, 24
amenable, 176
amnesty, 62
amorphous, 52
anathema, 110
annotation, 128
anomalous, 72
aplomb, 24
approbation, 14
archetype, 52
ascribe, 34
aspersion, 72
assuage, 14
astute, 110
aura, 52
austere, 90
autonomy, 62
avarice, 110
aver, 166
axiomatic, 62

bedlam, 128
beneficent, 90
berate, 176
bizarre, 72
blatant, 166
blazon, 62
bombastic, 24
bovine, 100
broach, 166
brouhaha, 186
brusque, 72
bulwark, 186
buttress, 166

cadaverous, 90
cajole, 72
callow, 24
caricature, 148
carnage, 176
carousal, 166
castigate, 72
caveat, 62
censurable, 138
choleric, 186
circuitous, 34
clangor, 148
cloy, 186
coalition, 14
collate, 167
commiserate, 34
concoct, 90
connoisseur, 167
consternation, 100
contiguous, 148
contingent, 138
contraband, 52
contrive, 72
corpulent, 100
corroborate, 138
covert, 128
crass, 90
credulous, 176
criterion, 176
culpable, 110
cupidity, 148
curtail, 186

debase, 90
debonair, 128
decadence, 14
deference, 187
definitive, 187
deleterious, 148
demagogue, 73
demeanor, 187
denizen, 138
deplete, 176
desecrate, 91
dilatory, 111
disabuse, 73
disavow, 100
disconcert, 91

disconsolate, 167
discursive, 138
dispassionate, 100
disseminate, 139
dissension, 101
dissipate, 101
dowdy, 139
drivel, 24
dun, 128

efficacious, 129
egregious, 111
elicit, 14
encumber, 167
enhance, 149
enigmatic, 187
enjoin, 35
ennui, 73
enthrall, 149
epitome, 24
equanimity, 129
equitable, 62
equivocate, 111
erudite, 53
evanescent, 111
exhort, 25
ex officio, 25
expatiate, 177
expedite, 35
expiate, 35
expostulate, 14
expurgate, 101
extenuate, 149
extraneous, 177
extricate, 62

ferment, 35
fetter, 73
filch, 63
florid, 139
flout, 63
foist, 139
foment, 167
fortuitous, 129
fractious, 63

gauche, 139
gauntlet, 101

gist, 129
gossamer, 53
grandiose, 91
gratuitous, 129
grisly, 167

hackneyed, 15
heinous, 73
herculean, 167
heresy, 139
hiatus, 15
hypothetical, 101

ignoble, 101
immutable, 73
impassive, 168
imperious, 129
implicit, 149
impromptu, 187
impugn, 101
inadvertent, 35
inauspicious, 168
inception, 177
incisive, 149
inconsequential, 91
incontrovertible, 168
inculcate, 139
infirmity, 177
infraction, 91
infringe, 25
ingratiate, 25
inimical, 149
innuendo, 15
inscrutable, 53
insular, 53
insurgent, 74
intemperate, 102
intercede, 15
interloper, 25
intrinsic, 25
invective, 129
inveigh, 25
irresolute, 111
irrevocable, 53

jaded, 15
jejune, 177

INDEX